# The
# Metallic Skills

# FOUNDATIONS OF SCIENCE LIBRARY

## The Natural World
*(4 volumes)*

The Majesty of the Heavens
*(Foundations of Astronomy)*

The Round World
*(Foundations of Geology and Geomorphology)*

The Skies and the Seas
*(Foundations of Meteorology, Oceanography & Cartography)*

The Ages of the Earth
*(Foundations of Palaeogeography and Palaeontology)*

## The Biological Sciences
*(6 volumes)*

The Life of Animals without Backbones
*(Foundations of Invertebrate Zoology)*

The Life of Animals with Backbones
*(Foundations of Vertebrate Zoology)*

The World of Plants
*(Foundations of Botany)*

Breeding and Growing
*(Foundations of Genetics, Anthropology and Agriculture)*

Patterns of Living
*(Foundations of Ecology)*

Human Kind
*(Foundations of Human Biology)*

## The Physical Sciences
*(9 volumes)*

The Restlessness of Matter
*(Foundations of Aerodynamics, Hydrodynamics and Thermodynamics)*

The Science of Movement
*(Foundations of Mechanics and Sound)*

Lightning in Harness
*(Foundations of Electricity)*

The Silent Energy
*(Foundations of Electrical Technology)*

The Cathode Ray Revolution
*(Foundations of Electronics)*

The Rays of Light
*(Foundations of Optics)*

The Unseen Spectrum
*(Foundations of Electromagnetic Radiation)*

The Cosmic Power
*(Foundations of Nuclear Physics)*

The Discipline of Numbers
*(Foundations of Mathematics)*

## The Chemical Sciences
*(4 volumes)*

The Fundamental Materials
*(Foundations of Basic Chemistry)*

The Elements and their Order
*(Foundations of Inorganic Chemistry)*

The Giant Molecules
*(Foundations of Organic Chemistry)*

The Chemist at Work
*(Foundations of Analysis and Laboratory Techniques)*

## Technology
*(5 volumes)*

The Metallic Skills
*(Foundations of Metallurgy)*

Industrial Processing
*(Foundations of Industrial and Chemical Technology)*

Engineering Technology
*(Foundations of Applied Engineering)*

Automobile Engineering
*(Foundations of Car Mechanics)*

The Inventive Genius
*(Foundations of Scientific Inventions)*

## History and Reference
*(3 volumes)*

The Beginnings of Science
*(Foundations of Scientific History)*

Frontiers of Science
*(Foundations of Research Methods)*

A Dictionary of Scientific Terms
*(The Foundations of Science Reference Book)*

# The Metallic Skills

## Foundations of Metallurgy

FOUNDATIONS OF SCIENCE LIBRARY

*TECHNOLOGY*

DISTRIBUTED IN THE U.S.A. BY
Ginn and Company : BOSTON
PUBLISHED BY
Sampson Low, Marston and Co : LONDON

This new presentation assembles
freshly edited material from
'Understanding Science' on one
subject into a single volume.

Library of Congress Catalog Card
Number: 66–17982

Catalog No.: L–20765

Made and printed in Great Britain by
Purnell & Sons Ltd., Paulton
(Somerset) and London

# METALLURGY

# Contents

# Introduction to

# Metallurgy

# Metallurgy and the Metallurgist

THE subject of metallurgy covers a vast field and the metallurgist today may find his work taking him all over the world, from the copper mines of the Congo to the steel works of Sheffield. The subject is so large that, while a student will learn something of all the aspects of metallurgy, when he has qualified he will usually specialise in that field or subject which interests him most.

Normally, metallurgy may be sub-divided into two parts: *ferrous metallurgy*, which is that dealing with iron and steel, and *non-ferrous metallurgy*, which covers the rest of the metals. The fact that iron and steel should be considered alone gives some idea of the size and importance of the iron and steel industry in the world. Iron is the most useful metal we have and, after aluminium, it is the most plentiful. Four parts in one hundred of the Earth's crust are iron.

With a few exceptions, such as gold, metals are not found in nature in the metallic state but as an *ore*, which may be an oxide, sulphide, or some other chemical combination of the metal. This ore must be mined and then processed until it is fit to go to the next stage of treatment. This is the job of the *extraction metallurgist*, and the methods employed differ with various ores.

The ore may be obtained initially by digging or blasting, but whichever method is used it usually comes in big lumps associated with a lot of earth and rubble, which must be removed. This process is known as *dressing the ore*.

Firstly, it is usually crushed into pieces of a manageable size. The next stage is the removal of the dirt and worthless matter and this is sometimes done by a process called *flotation*. This depends on the fact that different minerals have different *wetting charac-*

*No one wants accidents like the failure of this bridge. It is the job of the metallurgist to study metal failure and prevent it from happening.*

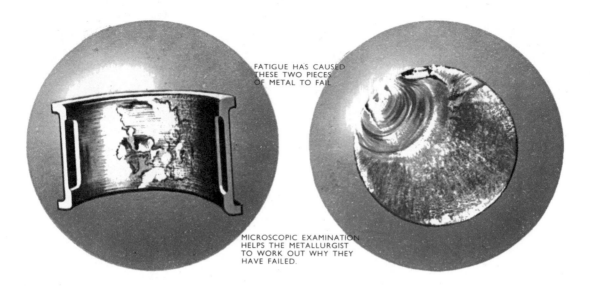

FATIGUE HAS CAUSED THESE TWO PIECES OF METAL TO FAIL

MICROSCOPIC EXAMINATION HELPS THE METALLURGIST TO WORK OUT WHY THEY HAVE FAILED.

*The electron microscope with magnifications of more than 100,000 is of great help to the metallurgist in studying metallic structures.*

*teristics* and under the right conditions in a bath of liquid, the valuable ore can be made to float off in a froth while the worthless rock sinks to the bottom, or sometimes the ore sinks. It is the job of the metallurgist to experiment in the laboratory on small samples of ore to find the best way of doing this and also control operations when they are performed on a large scale.

The next stage is to convert the ore to crude, impure metal. This is done by a process called *smelting*. Smelting furnaces differ in design depending on the ore to be treated, but the most widely known is probably the *blast furnace* used for iron.

It is the job of the metallurgist in the smelting works to ensure that this process runs correctly. He must analyse the iron ore fed in and calculate the quantities of coke and limestone needed to deal with it. Then he must examine the output of pig iron to make sure it is the correct quality.

From the smelting works the crude metal must then be purified or *refined*. This again may be done in one or more of a number of different ways. Sometimes the crude metal is remelted and air blown through it to oxidize the impurities and thus burn them off. Another method, as used for copper, is to cast the crude metal into slabs which are then refined by *electrolytic* methods.

The slabs are placed in a suitable chemical solution (containing copper sulphate) together with thin sheets of pure copper. They are then connected in circuit to a direct current supply, the impure slabs to the positive, the pure sheets to the negative. Pure copper is then removed by the passage of current from the impure slabs, now called the *anodes*, and deposited on the pure copper sheets, now called the *cathodes*. By controlling the voltage only the copper is deposited, the impurities either remaining in the bottom of the tank as a sludge or dissolving in the solution. Again, it is a metallurgical problem to find the best way of economically recovering any precious metals from the sludge at the bottom of the tank.

At the end of the refining process the relatively pure metal is obtained. This may now be used in its present form or remelted and mixed with another metal, or metals, to form an *alloy*. This may then be cast into a mould which is the shape of the finished pro-

*In the metallurgical laboratory, this section of rail which showed no signs of flaw was etched with acid, inked and a print taken of it. The flaw in the metal now shows up clearly.*

duct or a convenient shape for future processing. The work of melting and casting is carried out in a *foundry* and the metallurgist here is responsible for the control of the melting, alloying and casting procedures. He must also be experienced in mould design, and must be able to recognize and rectify faults that may appear in his castings.

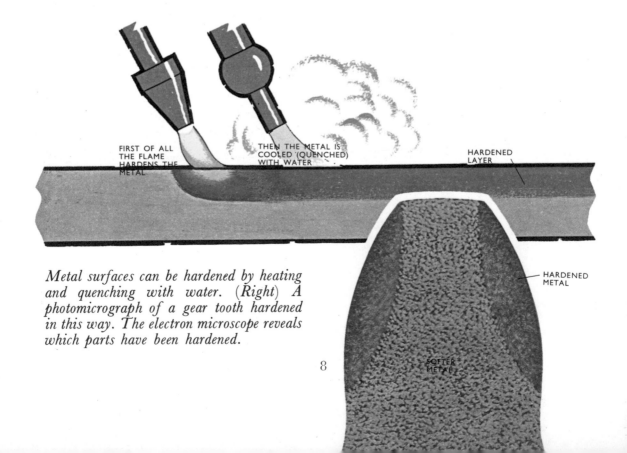

*Metal surfaces can be hardened by heating and quenching with water. (Right) A photomicrograph of a gear tooth hardened in this way. The electron microscope reveals which parts have been hardened.*

8

Metals which are not cast into their final shapes are usually cast into slabs or bars for further treatment by rolling, forging etc. This is known as *mechanical treatment*.

The metal or alloy may now be either rolled to sheet in a rolling mill, forged under a power hammer, or drawn to wire by pulling it through a series of *dies* of decreasing sizes. All these processes must be performed economically and the works metallurgist is responsible for seeing that this is done. He must calculate, for example, how much a slab of metal can be rolled before it needs *annealing*, or softening, in a furnace, as most metals become hard and will crack if they are worked too much. On the other hand annealing costs time and money and therefore must not be done more often than necessary.

Finally, one of the most important fields is research. This may be *applied research*, dealing with problems directly related to industry and the improvement of products, or it may be *fundamental research*, which is concerned with the basic reasons for metals behaving the way they do.

In industry the metallurgist may be called upon to solve a problem that is holding up a production line, or his more routine work may be to check the quality of products from the line.

Most of the equipment used and the methods employed however, are much the same whatever the nature of the research. Only the application of the results may differ. The industrial man may, for instance, measure the hardness of a piece of metal to ensure that the required standard is being maintained. His counterpart in pure research may use a change in that same property, which he can measure easily, to indicate a change that has occurred within the structure of the metal which he cannot see directly.

One of the most important tools available to the metallurgist is the microscope and the development of the electron microscope, with magnifications of more than 100,000 times, greatly aided the study of metallic structures.

Another very important field is the study of corrosion and the development of corrosion-resistant alloys for various applications. Most common metals are attacked and corroded under certain conditions. It may be sea water attacking the tubes in which steam from a ship's boilers is condensing or the attack of moist earth on underground electric cables. The damage caused by corrosion costs millions of pounds a year.

Future work in research looks even more interesting as space travel and the use of nuclear power are developed and it becomes impossible to use everyday materials at the high temperatures and conditions of radiation that will be encountered.

*Drilling operations preparatory to blasting out ore in a copper mine.*

# Metal Production

# CHAPTER TWO

# The Mineral Sources of Metals

THE metal which has probably played the most useful role in history in one form or another is iron. Most of the iron produced nowadays is in ferro-alloy form. Steel itself is an alloy of iron and carbon (with between 0·1 and 1·6% of the latter). But many types of steels are made to suit many different purposes by adding small quantities of other metals such as tungsten, cobalt, nickel, molybdenum, vanadium, chromium and manganese. The minerals of these metals are grouped together here under the heading 'Ferro-alloy Minerals'.

## FERRO-ALLOY MINERALS

### IRON

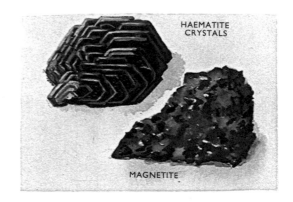

The most important ore of iron is haematite (an oxide of iron). In the common massive form, haematite is reddish-brown but the brilliant crystals (hexagonal rhombohedral) are black. A distinguishing feature of this mineral is its cherry-red streak (the colour when powdered). When in fine, shiny crystals haematite is called specularite, when in thin scales, micaceous haematite, and when in large kidney-shaped masses, kidney ore (hardness or H. 1 to 6 on Mohs scale; specific gravity or Sp. Gr. 5). Magnetite (also an oxide of iron), another important ore, is the only mineral which is strongly attracted to a magnet. One variety, lodestone, is itself a natural magnet. Magnetite occurs as iron-black crystals (isometric), as grains or in massive form. (H. 6; Sp. Gr. 5·2).

Less important ores of iron include limonite (hydrated oxide of iron) and siderite (iron carbonate). Limonite, an amorphous mineral (i.e. non-crystalline), is usually soft and earthy (yellow ochre), but also occurs in hard rounded masses (botryoidal). (H. 1 to 5·5; Sp. Gr. 3·5). Siderite, ranging from yellow to dark brown in colour, has a white streak and a pearly lustre. (H. 4; Sp. Gr. 3·8). The name is also applied to meteoric iron. Naturally occurring siderite is also called chalybite or spathic iron. Iron does occur as the native metal, but very rarely.

Pyrite, iron pyrites, or 'Fool's gold' (a sulphide of iron) is a hard brassy-yellow mineral which occurs as crystals (isometric, but in many forms), grains, or massive. It can be distinguished from gold by its greenish-black streak and greater hardness. (H. 6; Sp. Gr. 5). Strangely enough, pyrite does sometimes contain enough gold to make it a worthwhile ore. It is also used in the manufacture of sulphuric acid and, occasionally, as a source of iron. Marcasite (identical in composition to pyrite), sometimes called white pyrites, differs from pyrite in colour (pale yellow), tenacity (more brittle) and crystal form (orthorhombic). (H. 6; Sp. Gr. 4·8).

# TUNGSTEN

The principal use of tungsten is in the manufacture of steel for high speed cutting tools (tungsten has the highest melting point of all metals). Another important use is in the manufacture of filaments for light bulbs, radio tubes, etc. Tungsten carbide, an alloy only recently developed, is widely used in the manufacture of jet engines and super hard, long lasting, high speed cutting tools.

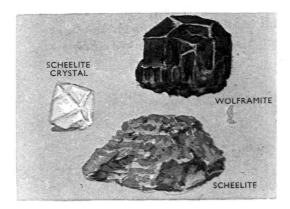

SCHEELITE CRYSTAL

WOLFRAMITE

SCHEELITE

The chief sources of tungsten are scheelite (calcium tungstate) and wolframite (a tungstate of iron and manganese). Scheelite, a glassy, usually colourless mineral, fluoresces blue under short-wave ultra-violet light. It occurs in massive form or in tetragonal crystals (usually double pyramids). (H. 5; Sp. Gr. 6).

Wolframite often occurs as grains or monoclinic crystals (tabular or prismatic). It is brownish-black in colour, heavy and brittle. (H. 5·5; Sp. Gr. 7·5). A less important ore is huebnerite (a tungstate of manganese) which occurs in massive form or as monoclinic crystals. It is brownish-black in colour with a brownish-yellow streak. (H. 5·5; Sp. Gr. 7).

# COBALT

The principal use of cobalt is in the manufacture of rustless alloys, alloys capable of withstanding high temperatures, and remarkably permanent magnets.

Most of the world's cobalt is obtained as a by-product from ores which are worked chiefly for the other metals they contain. Hence most comes from the copper mines of Katanga and Zambia. Formerly, the chief source of this metal were the minerals cobaltite (sulphide and arsenide of cobalt) and smaltite (cobalt diarsenide). Cobaltite crystallizes in the isometric system but usually occurs in massive form. It is brittle, and silver in colour. (H. 5·5; Sp. Gr. 6·3). Smaltite resembles arsenopyrite (an ore of arsenic) in many ways and chemical tests are needed to distinguish between them. Cobalt bloom (erythrite) a beautiful, peach-red mineral is formed by the weathering of cobalt ores.

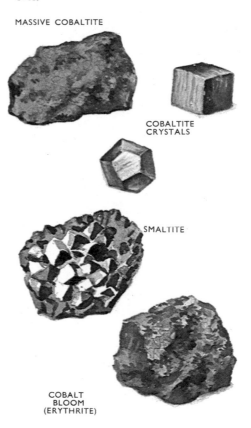

MASSIVE COBALTITE

COBALTITE CRYSTALS

SMALTITE

COBALT BLOOM (ERYTHRITE)

# CHROMIUM

Two very important uses of chromium arc in the manufacture of stainless steels and various alloys and to provide a shiny, non-tarnish coating on less presentable metals, such as iron.

CHROMITE

13

Chromium is essentially a one-ore metal. Chromite (an oxide of iron and chromium) is a brownish-black, brittle mineral, associated with ultra-basic rocks (very heavy igneous rocks). Crystals (isometric) are rare, chromite usually being massive and granular (H. 5·5; Sp. Gr. 4·5).

The chief ore of nickel is pentlandite (a sulphide of iron and nickel) which usually occurs with pyrrhotite (iron sulphide) from which it is very difficult to distinguish. Pentlandite is bronze in colour and crystallizes in the isometric system, though it usually occurs in massive form (H. 3·5 to 4; Sp. Gr. 4·6). Minor nickel ores are niccolite (nickel arsenide) and millerite, or nickel pyrites (nickel sulphide). Niccolite is commonly massive and copper-red in colour with a dark brown streak. (H. 5·5; Sp. Gr. 7·5). Millerite sometimes occurs as brassy-yellow slender crystals.

## NICKEL

More than half of the nickel produced is used in the steel industry, particularly in the production of stainless steels. Steel containing 25 to 32% nickel has a high electrical resistance and is thus widely used for the elements of electric fires, cookers, etc. With a 36% nickel content, steel becomes 'invar' the alloy which expands and contracts very little with temperature changes and is used for extremely accurate measuring tapes. Permalloy and alnico, both nickel alloys, are used in making permanent magnets. British 'silver' coins are one-quarter nickel. The American 5-cent piece, popularly called a 'nickel' is 25% nickel and 75% copper.

## MANGANESE

Manganese is important in the actual process of smelting steel where it acts as a cleanser. It is also extensively used to toughen steel for rails, machinery, armour plate, etc.

Most of the world production of manganese comes from two black minerals, pyrolusite (manganese dioxide) and psilomelane (an impure hydrated oxide of manganese). Pyrolusite may be soft and earthy, granular, fibrous or crystalline. The little gleaming black individual crystals are very rare. (H. 1 to 6 according to form; Sp. Gr. 5). Psilomelane occurs in a number of forms (massive, botryoidal, stalactitic) though crystals are unknown. It may be distinguished from pyrolusite by its greater hardness. (H. 5 to 6; Sp. Gr. 4·2). Minor ores are manganite (hydrated oxide of manganese) and rhodochrosite (carbonate of manganese).

PYROLUSITE

RHODOCROSITE

MANGANITE
CRYSTALS

PSILOMELANE

PENTLANDITE

NICCOLITE

FIBROUS
MILLERITE

## MOLYBDENUM

WULFENITE CRYSTALS

Molybdenum is a metal widely used in the manufacture of tool steels. It is also of considerable importance in the manufacture of special steels used in aircraft and automobiles.

Molybdenum is obtained from two minerals, molybdenite (molybdenum sulphide), which is by far the most important, and wulfenite (lead molybdate). Molybdenite is a very soft, lead-grey, brilliant mineral with a greasy feel. It occurs as flecks or tabular crystals (hexagonal). (H. 1 to 1·5; Sp. Gr. 4·7). Wulfenite is often found as yellow or orange tetragonal crystals (tabular, prismatic, or double pyramids). (H. 3; Sp. Gr. 6·7).

MOLYBDENITE

## VANADIUM

VANADINITE

Vanadium is a metal which is used almost exclusively in the steel industry, for special alloy steels, for locomotive and automobile forgings, axles, driving shafts, etc. Spring steels contain a very small percentage of vanadium.

The most important vanadium minerals are carnotite (a hydrous vanadate of potassium and uranium), descloizite (a hydrous vanadate of lead, copper and zinc) and vanadinite (a chloride and vanadate of lead). Carnotite, remarkable for its canary-yellow colour, usually forms earthy masses and is radioactive. (H. 1; Sp. Gr. 4·1). Descloizite crystallizes in the ortho-rhombic system (the crystals are usually double pyramids) and also occurs in massive form. The colour is usually dark brown but the streak reddish-orange. Vanadinite is an attractive mineral, ranging from ruby-red to yellow and brown in colour. It usually occurs as hexagonal, prismatic crystals. (H. 3; Sp. Gr. 7).

CARNOTITE

## MORE METALLIC MINERALS

### GOLD

Gold, the 'king of metals' and the basis of trade nearly everywhere, is one of the few metals which occurs frequently in the native state, i.e. uncombined with other elements (though in practice other metals, particularly silver, are present). Gold is found in quartz veins; but as the

deposits are eroded, the heavy gold becomes concentrated in stream beds and can be recovered by washing away the lighter sand.

Native gold (hardness or H. 2·5 on Mohs scale; specific gravity or Sp. Gr. 19·3) is soft, heavy, and yellow in colour. In rocks, gold occurs as flecks or plates, the isometric crystals being rare. Another source of the metal is

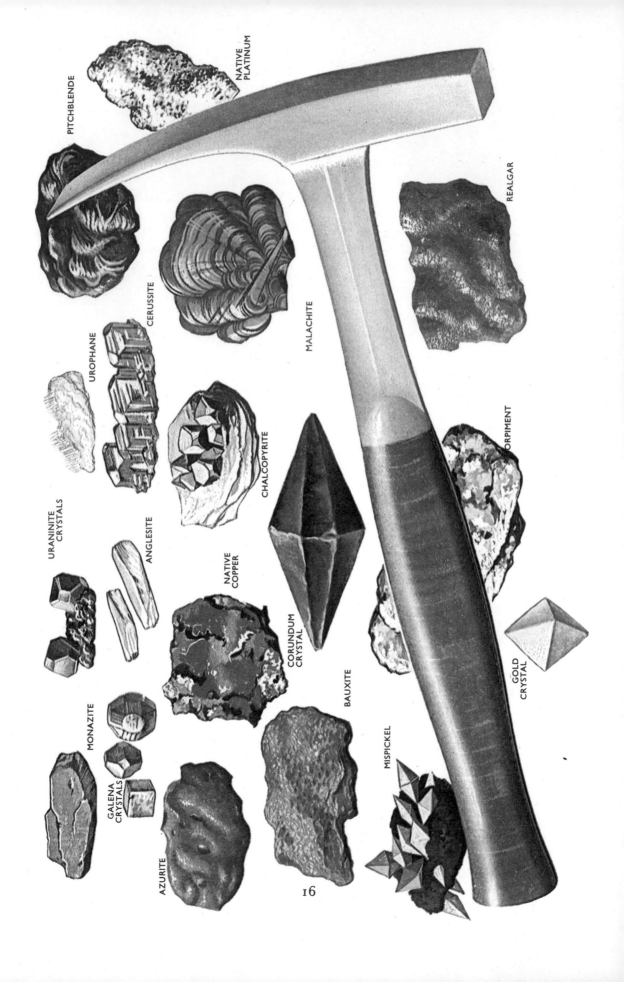

PITCHBLENDE

NATIVE PLATINUM

REALGAR

CERUSSITE

UROPHANE

MALACHITE

ORPIMENT

CHALCOPYRITE

URANINITE CRYSTALS

ANGLESITE

NATIVE COPPER

CORUNDUM CRYSTAL

GOLD CRYSTAL

MONAZITE

BAUXITE

GALENA CRYSTALS

MISPICKEL

AZURITE

16

calaverite (gold telluride), a brittle mineral ranging from yellow to silver in colour. (H. 2·5 to 3; Sp. Gr. about 9.) Gold is also recovered from other minerals.

## SILVER

A metal which has played a far greater role in commerce in the past than in the present is silver. The amount used for coinage purposes has fallen drastically in recent years. Today three-quarters of the silver produced is used in industry. One very important use is in the manufacture of photographic films. More than half of the world's silver is obtained as a by-product of lead, zinc and copper production, while gold mines yield an appreciable amount.

Like gold, silver occurs in the native state (H. 2·5 to 3; Sp. Gr. 10·5), but the chief source of the metal is argentite (silver sulphide), a shiny, lead-grey mineral, often associated with native silver, and lead, zinc and copper minerals. It crystallizes in the isometric system but usually occurs in massive form. (H. 2·5; Sp. Gr. 7·3.)

## LEAD

Often associated with silver is the much more humble metal lead. About one-third of the world production of this metal is used in accumulators, e.g. automobile batteries. Other important uses are in the manufacture of paints and cable coverings, and for constructional purposes.

Lead does occur in the native state, but by far the most important source of the metal is the mineral galena (lead sulphide). This is a brittle, silver-grey mineral which commonly forms cubic crystals. Galena is notable for its perfect cubic cleavage. (H. 2·5; Sp. Gr. 7·5.) Less important ores of lead are cerussite (lead carbonate) and anglesite (sulphate of lead). Cerussite sometimes forms needle-like bundles of large white crystals, but usually occurs in massive form. (H. 3·5; Sp. Gr. 6·5.) Anglesite, formed by the oxidation of galena, is usually colourless or grey and has an adamantine lustre. (H. 3; Sp. Gr. 6·3.)

## ZINC

Zinc is a metal which naturally follows on from lead, for the two are intimately connected. In fact there is only one important zinc deposit which contains no lead ore, and workable quantities of both are usually present in the same mine. By far the chief use of zinc is in providing a rust-proof coating on iron. Brass is an alloy of copper and zinc.

The chief source of zinc is the mineral sphalerite, otherwise known as zinc blende or black-jack (zinc sulphide). Sphalerite, meaning deceptive, is a good name, for its colour ranges from black to red, brown, green and yellow. Crystals (isometric) are common and cleavage in six directions is perfect. (H. 3·5 to 4; Sp. Gr. 4.) Other zinc ores include zincite (zinc oxide), smithsonite (zinc carbonate), hemimorphite (hydrous silicate of zinc), willemite (zinc silicate) and franklinite (a variety of magnetite). Zincite (H. 4 to 4·5; Sp. Gr. 5·5), an orange-red mineral, and franklinite are confined to a single locality. Smithsonite varies considerably in colour and often occurs in honey-comb or stalactitic masses (H. 5; Sp. Gr. 4·4).Willemite (H. 5 to 6; Sp. Gr. about 4) varies in colour but will nearly always fluoresce bright green under ultra-violet light. Hemimorphite (H. 4·5 to 5; Sp. Gr. about 3·5) may be brown, yellow, blue or white in colour. The name calamine has been applied to both hemimorphite and smithsonite.

## THORIUM

Thorium is a metal which probably has an important future in the field of atomic energy, but at present its main use lies in the chemical industry and in the manufacture of gas-mantles.

The two most important sources of thorium are monazite (a complex mineral containing thorium) and thorite (thorium silicate). Monazite occurs as monoclinic crystals and as grains in 'heavy' sands. Brownish-yellow and brittle, it is strongly radioactive. (H. 5 to 5·5; Sp. Gr. 5.) Thorite, ranging from red to black in colour, usually occurs in massive form. (H. 5; Sp. Gr. 5 to 6.)

## URANIUM

Uranium has recently become a valuable source of atomic power. Strangely enough, this highly prized element is widely scattered throughout the Earth's crust in igneous rocks. But workable deposits are few and far between and the search for uranium has rivalled the 'gold rushes' of former days.

> There are many uranium-bearing minerals but few are of commercial importance. Uraninite (an impure oxide of uranium) is a hard, heavy, black mineral, occurring in isometric crystals. (H. 5·5; Sp. Gr. 9 to 9·7.) Pitchblende is a massive variety of uraninite. Carnotite, already described as an ore of vanadium, is another important ore. Urophane (a complex uranium-bearing mineral) often occurs with uraninite as tiny straw-yellow, needle-like orthorhombic crystals. (H. 2 to 3; Sp. Gr. 3·8.) All uranium minerals are radio-active.

## COPPER

Copper was probably the first metal to be smelted from its ore, a process which is fairly simple. The alloy bronze (copper and tin) was probably discovered accidentally because in many places the two metals occur together. Owing to its low electrical resistance, the chief use of copper is in the electrical industry.

> Copper forms more minerals than any other metal but only a few are important ores. The chief sources are the sulphides of the metal

chalcopyrite (sulphide of copper and iron), chalcocite (cuprous sulphide) and bornite (copper iron sulphide). Chalcopyrite (H. 3·5 to 4; Sp. Gr. 4·2) is a brassy mineral with a greenish-black streak. It is usually found in massive form. Chalcocite (H. 2·5; Sp. Gr. 5·5) is lead-grey in colour and has a conchoidal fracture. Its orthorhombic crystals are rare. Bornite (H. 3; Sp. Gr. 5), sometimes called peacock ore owing to a frequent blue or purple tarnish, is bronze coloured when freshly exposed and has a black streak. Once again crystals (isometric) are rare. Other names for bornite are erubescite and variegated copper ore. The weathering of copper minerals at the surface is responsible for the attractive carbonates malachite and azurite (green and blue respectively). The difference between these two lies simply in their water content—8·2% in the former and 5·2% in the latter. (H. 4; Sp. Gr. 3·8 to 4, for both.)

## ALUMINIUM

Aluminium is one of the most versatile of metals. Being very light (about one-third as dense as iron), non-corrosive and, in alloy form, mechanically strong, it is an ideal aircraft construction metal.

> Despite the fact that aluminium is the most common metal in the Earth's crust almost all of the world's production comes from just one

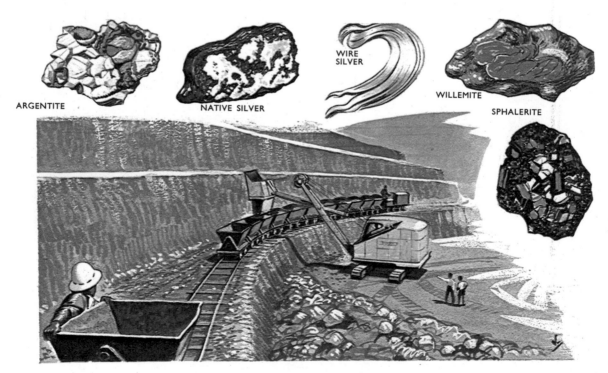

ARGENTITE

NATIVE SILVER

WIRE SILVER

WILLEMITE

SPHALERITE

*Open-cast mining of ore-bearing rock.*

mineral—bauxite (a mixture of hydrated aluminium oxides). This is formed by the weathering of aluminium-bearing rocks in a tropical climate. Though white or buff by nature the presence of iron stains it reddish-brown. (H. 3 or below; Sp. Gr. 2·5.)

Other aluminium minerals, though not a source of the metal, are commercially important. Kaolinite (hydrated aluminium silicate), otherwise known as china clay, usually occurs as white earthy masses. This mineral is of vital importance to the ceramic industry. (H. 2 to 2·5; Sp. Gr. 2·6.) Cryolite ( a fluoride of sodium and aluminium) is a rare mineral which was once of vital importance in aluminium refining. Nowadays, artificial cryolite is used. Corundum (aluminium oxide) is a grey to brown mineral frequently forming hexagonal crystals. When richly coloured, corundum is a highly prized gemstone. (H. 9—harder than any other common mineral; Sp. Gr. 4.)

## PLATINUM

Platinum is the commonest member of a group of metals including palladium, osmium, iridium, ruthenium and rhodium. It is widely used in jewellery, but also has electrical, dental and chemical uses.

Platinum does occur as the native metal, usually as grains or nuggets in placer deposits. It is very heavy, malleable, and grey in colour. (H. 4 to 4·5; Sp. Gr. 21·5 when pure.) Sperrylite (platinum arsenide) is a valuable platinum ore. It is hard, heavy, white in colour and has a black streak. Sperrylite sometimes forms large isometric crystals (H. 6 to 7; Sp. Gr. 10·5).

## ARSENIC

Metallic arsenic has few uses, the chief one being the hardening of lead shot. But arsenic trioxide is used in enormous quantities in insecticides and weed-killers. Lead arsenate is extensively used against the cotton boll weevil and copper or lead arsenate against the potato bug.

The chief ore of arsenic is arsenopyrite, also called mispickel (sulpharsenide of iron). This steel-grey ore is usually found in crystalline masses. Individual crystals are small and wedge-shaped (H. 5·5 to 6; Sp. Gr. 6). Far more spectacular are the minerals orpiment (arsenic trisulphide) and realgar (arsenic sulphide). The former is yellow in colour, the latter vivid red (H. 1·5 to 2; Sp. Gr. 3·5 for both). Both were once used as pigments for paints.

## TIN

The most common use of tin is in coating the iron of 'tin' cans with an extremely thin protective layer to prevent rusting. Fully 40% of the world production of tin is used in this manner despite the fact that the film of tin accounts for only 1% of a can's weight. Large quantities are also used in alloys and solders.

Like aluminium, tin has just one ore—cassiterite (tin oxide). This forms tetragonal crystals (prisms and pyramids) but usually occurs as granular masses or fibrous masses (wood tin). It is quite brittle and has a brilliant lustre. (H. 6 to 7; Sp. Gr. 7.)

CINNABAR CRYSTAL

ILMENITE CRYSTAL

COLUMBITE

## MERCURY

Mercury is the only metal which is liquid at normal temperatures. It is extensively used in the preparation of drugs and chemicals and in scientific instruments. The most well-known use, in thermometers, represents only a small fraction of the total consumption.

The only source of mercury is cinnabar (mercuric sulphide), a bright red mineral which forms hexagonal crystals, though it is usually found in massive form, or as scattered flecks. It has a scarlet-red streak (H. 2·5; Sp. Gr. 8·1). Native mercury is sometimes found in cinnabar.

## TITANIUM

Owing to its light weight and high melting point titanium is being used in ever-increasing quantities in a number of different fields—rocket construction, for instance. It is also used in the manufacture of paints.

The chief ores of titanium are rutile (titanium dioxide) and ilmenite (oxide of iron and titanium). Rutile often crystallizes as tetragonal prismatic crystals, black or reddish brown in colour. It is found in igneous or metamorphic rocks. (H. 6; Sp .Gr. 4·2.) Ilmenite, black in colour, may be found massive or as grains or flecks. Crystals are rare. It is often associated with magnetite. (H. 5 to 6; Sp. Gr. 4·5.)

## MAGNESIUM

Owing to its lightness, magnesium is extensively used in alloy form with aluminium and other metals for lightweight construction purposes.

The principal ores of magnesium are magnesite (magnesium carbonate) and dolomite (a carbonate of calcium and magnesium). Magnesite is usually crystalline or granular and individual crystals are rare. It ranges in colour from white to yellow and brown. (H. 4; Sp. Gr. 3.) Dolomite (a carbonate of calcium and magnesium) is a minor ore of magnesium.

CASSITERITE

CASSITERITE CRYSTALS

MASSIVE CINNABAR

RUTILE MASSIVE COLUMNAR

RUTILE STRIATED CRYSTAL

MAGNESITE

DOLOMITE

STIBNITE

## ANTIMONY

Antimony is widely used for hardening lead and making it resistant to corrosion in the form of battery plates, lead sheet and lead pipes. Type metal is a lead-antimony alloy with small amounts of tin and sometimes copper.

The chief source of antimony is the mineral stibnite, sometimes called antimonite or antimony glance (antimony trisulphide). This lead-grey, brittle mineral sometimes forms distinctive slender prismatic crystals (orthorhombic system) but more often occurs in columnar masses. (H.2; Sp. Gr. 4·6.)

## COLUMBIUM TANTALUM

Columbium (or niobium) and tantalum are rare metals of considerable importance. They are used, for instance, in high-temperature alloys suitable for rocket engines, and in nuclear reactors.

Columbite and tantalite are complex ores of columbium and tantalum. Which name is given to the mineral simply depends upon whether columbium or tantalum is present in the greatest quantities. (H. 6; Sp. Gr. 5·5 to 8.)

CHAPTER THREE

# Iron and Steel

### Iron

Primitive man found that by lighting wood fires on top of lumps of iron ore he could extract the metal, iron. This worked best when gusts of high wind blew through the fire, fanning it into great heat. The ore contained iron oxides from which the carbon in the firewood robbed oxygen, and spongy iron was left behind.

The blast furnaces of today work on similar principles. They are so named because instead of being fanned by a high wind, *blasts* of hot air are blown through them.

The ore is fed into the furnace from the top along with coke and limestone. A hot blast of air entering at the bottom of the furnace reacts with the coke. This reaction produces carbon monoxide gas and gives

out great heat. Carbon monoxide acts as a reducing agent. In effect the ore is split into iron and oxygen. The molten iron flows down the furnace while the oxygen combines with the carbon monoxide to form carbon dioxide which goes up the furnace. The purpose of the limestone is largely to remove impurities such as sand. It combines with them as 'slag' which floats on the molten iron like a scum.

In the olden days molten iron was poured into hollows in a sand pit and allowed to solidify. Because the shapes of these solid slabs resemble pigs, the iron was known as *pig iron* and this name still persists. But most molten iron from the furnace goes on to another part of the works to be made into steel.

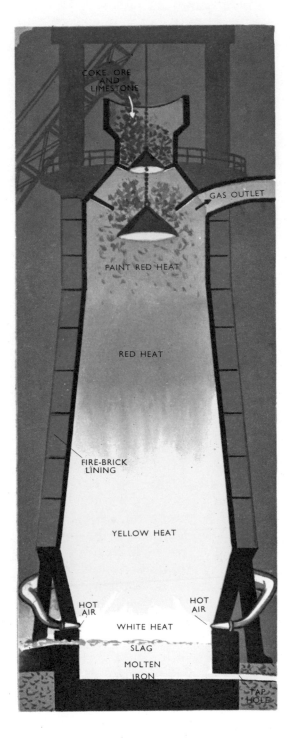

COKE, ORE AND LIMESTONE

GAS OUTLET

FAINT RED HEAT

RED HEAT

FIRE-BRICK LINING

YELLOW HEAT

HOT AIR

HOT AIR

WHITE HEAT

SLAG

MOLTEN IRON

TAP HOLE

*Section through a blast furnace.*

In 1855 Henry Bessemer in England found that when a blast of cold air was blown through molten iron, the carbon and other impurities were rapidly oxidized and blown away as gases. He patented his Bessemer converter for doing this on a large scale. Although it is now largely replaced by the *open hearth* process and other modern methods of steelmaking, considerable quantities of steel are still made in Bessemer converters.

Molten pig iron from the blast furnace is poured into the egg-shaped vessel and cold air blown in at the bottom roars its way up through the molten iron. At first there is nothing much to see, but after a few minutes flames begin to spout from the mouth of the converter. The sheet of flame grows brighter and brighter, often jumping about 40–50 feet in the air in a fantastic firework display. This Bessemer *blow* is one of the most spectacular sights of heavy industry.

Within the iron, silicon, manganese and carbon are being oxidized giving out great heat. Carbon monoxide gas rising through the molten iron makes it look as though it is boiling. After about 20 minutes the flame drops. Now no carbon is left. Air is blown through for 2 or 3 more minutes to burn out the phosphorus, during which time brown clouds of its oxides come off. The air supply is stopped and samples are taken to make sure the oxidation is complete.

As all the carbon has been removed, some must be put back. A calculated quantity or an alloy of manganese, iron and carbon is added. The manganese reacts with any iron that has been oxidized by the air blast and floats up to the surface as a slag. The iron has now become steel. Before this it was turbulent and bubbling, but after, it is quite calm. Because of this change, the final addition of alloy is known as *killing*. The hot steel is poured out into a ladle.

## Open Hearth Process

Although it has the advantage of speed, the huge quantities of scrap steel available cannot be used by the Bessemer converter, but they can in the open hearth process. With this process it is also possible to control the quality of the steel more accurately. Consequently despite the

*Molten pig iron from the blast furnace being poured into an open hearth furnace.*

*Diagram of an open hearth furnace. Gas and air pass through heating chambers and burn above the molten iron in the hearth, heating it and oxidizing its impurities. On their way out, the hot spent gases pass their heat to two more heating chambers. After a while the flow is reversed.*

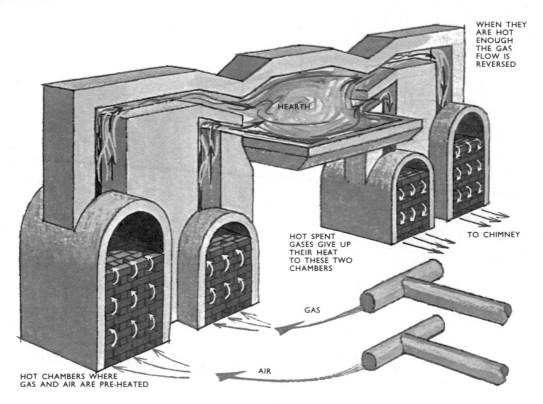

WHEN THEY ARE HOT ENOUGH THE GAS FLOW IS REVERSED

HEARTH

HOT SPENT GASES GIVE UP THEIR HEAT TO THESE TWO CHAMBERS

TO CHIMNEY

GAS

AIR

HOT CHAMBERS WHERE GAS AND AIR ARE PRE-HEATED

much longer time involved, most steel is now made in open hearths.

The Bessemer converter is a great waster of heat. When the flames leap from it, enormous quantities of heat are lost. The Siemens brothers realized that if this heat was properly utilized, the converter could be run at a much higher temperature, a temperature high enough in fact to melt cold scrap steel fed into the molten iron. The brothers designed the open hearth to do just this.

The open hearth furnace consists of a shallow steel bath lined with re-fractory bricks. At the back is a tap hole for emptying it.

Four heat storing chambers (two on either side) are connected to the fur-nace. These are filled with a chequered pattern of firebricks designed to retain the heat.

Limestone is fed into the empty furnace followed immediately by scrap steel. The hot flame of producer gas or oil burning in a stream of hot air is directed down on to the surface to heat and partially melt the scrap steel. After they have wafted over the sur-face the hot gases pass on to heat up the two brick chambers on the far side. Last of all, ladles of gurgling molten iron are poured in. The flames con-tinue to heat the mixture. The lime-

*A Bessemer converter spouting flame as the impurities in its charge of molten iron are oxidized. Cold air is blown in at the bottom of the converter.*

stone decomposes, giving off carbon dioxide which bubbles up to the surface of the writhing mass. When all is melted, the impurities are removed by the addition of oxidizing agents such as iron ore. In some cases oxygen is injected into the furnace to assist this oxidation.

Just as with the Bessemer converter, heat is given out as impurities are oxidized. The heat is used to heat up one pair of heating chambers. Then when these two chambers are sufficiently hot, the flow is reversed. The hot chambers heat the gas and air supplies while the other two chambers are being heated up by the waste gases

in readiness for heating the fuel and air when the flow is reversed again.

During this final refining, the various additional substances are added and the contents are sampled from time to time. The whole process takes between 8 and 20 hours after which the furnace is tapped and the glowing metal flows out into a brick lined ladle. The slag floating on the top overflows into another ladle.

In the last decade, there have been many technological changes in steel making. One of these has been the injection of large quantities of oxygen through the mouth of vessels similar to the Bessemer. This permits a higher

*Emptying an open hearth furnace. The slag collecting above the molten iron spills over into a second ladle.*

*A steel ingot being removed from a soaking pit where it has been reheated for some hours to bring it to an even temperature throughout. After soaking the steel is ready for working into shape.*

cess can therefore be more accurately controlled and, if necessary, strongly reducing conditions can be maintained.

There are two ways in which a furnace can be heated electrically – either by an *electric arc* or by *induction*. The electric arc is used for refining steel and the lesser-used induction process, for melting down specially selected scrap steel of the correct composition for making into articles such as ball bearings.

The *arc furnace* is a cylindrical bath made to hold from 10 to 30 tons of steel. It is first charged with lime to form an oxidizing slag which gathers up impurities. Specially selected scrap of known composition follows. Three carbon electrodes fitted in the furnace roof are lowered to make contact with the metal surface. Special transformers supply them with power. The scrap steel completes the circuit and the current flows. Immediately, the electrodes are raised so that they just lose contact with the steel. The current is then forced to jump the gap, and an electric arc is drawn between the electrodes and the steel, generating great heat. It takes over an hour for the charge to melt and the impurities to enter the slag. The carbon content remains almost correct and unaltered. The oxidizing slag is replaced by a reducing slag to remove any sulphur and oxygen. Then carefully regulated quantities of alloys are added and a sample of steel is analysed to make sure that the composition is exactly right.

The *induction furnace* deals with much smaller quantities of scrap. Here there is no direct electrical contact with the steel. An alternating current passes through a coil round the outside of the furnace, inducing eddy currents to flow inside the scrap. Heat is created.

rate of production, and in other new processes the steelmaking vessel is rotated to assist oxidation of the impurities and again accelerate output.

Using electricity for heating cuts out the oxidation by air and also the need for strong deoxidizers. The pro-

The currents also stir the mixture, making it uniform throughout. The greater the frequency with which the current changes direction the greater the heat produced in the steel. Consequently, current of high frequency is used.

Ladles of steel from furnaces of all types empty their liquid contents into huge iron moulds. The molten steel gradually cools down and solidifies to form an *ingot*. The cooling is uneven. The outside cools more rapidly than the inside. Also, flaws and hollows can develop inside the ingot due to shrinkage. Placing a neck of firebrick round the top of the ingot concentrates the cavities to the upper part. The flaw ridden section can later be sawn off and returned to the furnace for re-melting with another batch of steel.

When the red-hot ingots are stripped of their moulds, because they are unevenly heated they are not in a fit state to be worked. Huge tongs transport them to *soaking pits*, brick lined furnaces where they stay for hours until they are finally brought to an even temperature. Mammoth rollers then squeeze the steel to give it a suitable

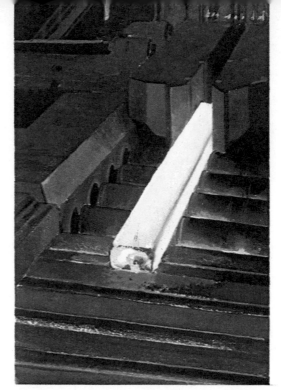

*An ingot undergoing treatment in a rolling mill.*

shape for further working. The rolling also strengthens the steel. Afterwards the final shape is given to the steel in one of three ways, hammering, rolling or pressing according to the type of steel and the shape of the article being made from it.

CHAPTER FOUR

# Copper

COPPER is one of the few *elements* to be found in the Earth's crust. But although native copper crystals are of interest to the geologist they are not present in sufficient quantities to be of great commercial importance. Most copper is found in copper ores where it is often combined with iron and sulphur. This is not surprising for copper, iron and sulphur were all belched up from the molten core of the Earth together, fighting their way through seams and cracks and often penetrating the pores of rocks. The world's main sources of copper are in the U.S.A., Zambia (Northern Rhodesia), Chile and Canada.

About $3\frac{1}{2}$ million tons of copper are smelted annually, over 25% of which is scrap copper being re-used. The rest is obtained from ores. The most commonly used ore is *chalcopyrite*

27

which, if it is pure, contains about $34\frac{1}{2}\%$ copper. However, because of all the other dirt mixed with the mineral, the ore that is mined usually contains no more than 1 or 2% of copper. Richer copper ores may contain up to 5%.

Most copper has to be mined by sinking deep shafts into the ground and driving tunnels through to the ore-bearing face. Explosives are used to loosen the ore which is sometimes crushed before taking it to the surface. Occasionally it lies near enough to the surface to strip off the covering layer of soil and rock, and enable it to be mined open-cast.

Some low grade ores and oxidized ores are often not mined but instead have the copper dissolved out of them. Dilute acid is poured over the ore and collected when it has drained through. Later, the liquid is put in large vats with lumps of iron. The iron takes

the place of the copper in solution and the copper comes out. It is later further refined.

The sulphide ores coming from the mines contain such a high percentage of rubbish and such a low percentage of useful mineral that the two must first be separated. The ore is crushed into 5-inch lumps between the gigantic jaws of powerful crushers and then passed through a kind of sieve called a *grizzly* to remove the smaller pieces which do not need further crushing. The 5-inch lumps are crushed to $1\frac{1}{2}$ inches by a cone crusher. This is a large strong pear-shaped steel vessel. Inside it is a huge pestle which rotates, grinding the ore. The pestle is a very loose fit at the top of the vessel and a much tighter fit at the bottom. Falling lumps of ore are crushed against the sides of the vessel becoming increasingly smaller as they fall. Further crushing in a similar vessel

*Cone crusher in which 5-inch lumps of ore are crushed to $1\frac{1}{2}$-inches.*

*Ball mill. The bombarding of the steel balls grinds the ore to a powder.*

28

*Flotation cells in which the mineral is separated from unwanted material. The mineral floats in a froth whereas the dirt sinks.*

reduces them to $\frac{1}{2}$-inch lumps. Finally they are reduced to a powder in a ball mill. This is a rotating drum containing a lot of steel balls which rattle round it bombarding and grinding the ore.

The mineral particles can now be separated from the dirt by *flotation*. Water makes particles of dirt sink to the bottom. The mineral is buoyed up and floats. To help this process pine oil is added to the water and the water is whisked into a froth. The useful mineral is carried along in the froth which is skimmed off while the unwanted dirt sinks to the bottom. The water is cleaned and used again. The *concentrate* of copper ore is filtered and ready for smelting. The concentrate often also contains gold and silver. The treatment from now on depends upon the type of ore being used. Native copper, oxide and carbonate concentrates may be smelted without further treatment but sulphur and iron-containing concentrates have to be *roasted* first. The roasting which takes place in a furnace has the effect

of drying the concentrate and driving off some of the sulphur as sulphur dioxide gas. The hot powder resulting from this treatment is known as *calcine*. It is a mixture of copper sulphide, iron sulphide and iron oxide.

*Smelting.* The purpose of smelting is to remove unwanted earthy constituents. Limestone is used for this because it combines chemically with the earth, forming slag. Combination also takes place between the unwanted iron oxide and the silicon dioxide in the earth.

$$\underset{\text{limestone}}{CaCO_3} + \underset{\substack{\text{silicon} \\ \text{dioxide}}}{SiO_2} \rightarrow \underset{\text{slag}}{CaSiO_3} + \underset{\substack{\text{carbon} \\ \text{dioxide}}}{CO_2}$$

$$\underset{\substack{\text{iron} \\ \text{oxide}}}{FeO} + \underset{\substack{\text{silicon} \\ \text{dioxide}}}{SiO_2} \rightarrow \underset{\text{slag}}{FeSiO_3}$$

The smelting nearly always takes place in coal, oil or gas-fired brick lined furnaces although there are a few electrically heated ones. The latest methods, however, involve using

29

the heat given out by the chemical reactions. This is known as *flash smelting*. Here, the dry calcine is blown into the furnace by gusts of air or oxygen. The heat given out by the reaction is sufficient to start the reaction of the charge blown in. The liquids in the furnace settle into two layers. Slag floats on top of the copper-containing *matte* layer. The slag is run off from time to time.

The matte is ladled into a *converter* in which the copper is finally set free. Air under pressure is blown through the molten matte, a mixture of copper sulphide and iron sulphide. The sulphur is blown away as sulphur dioxide gas and the iron is removed as a slag by the addition of sand. Although the air blown through is cold this does not cool the molten matte because once more the heat given out by the chemical reactions counteracts this. After several hours of aeration, the copper is cast into blistery cakes known as *blister copper*. Although blister copper is above 98% pure this is not pure enough.

Further *refining* takes place. Molten blister copper has more air blown through to oxidize and blow away any other impurities such as arsenic. In the course of this some of the copper is also oxidized and has to be changed back to copper by the reducing action of wooden poles which are fed into the furnace. The molten copper is again cast into blocks; this time called anodes because they are to be connected as anodes in the refining by *electrolysis*.

The electrolytic tank is filled with acidified copper sulphate solution and sheets of pure copper form the cathodes. Under the influence of a direct electric current copper 'dissolves' from the anode and deposits itself on the cathode. The impurities do not, and form a slimy mud underneath the anode.

*Converter in which the copper is set free from its compounds.*

*Electrolytic tank in which the copper is finally purified.*

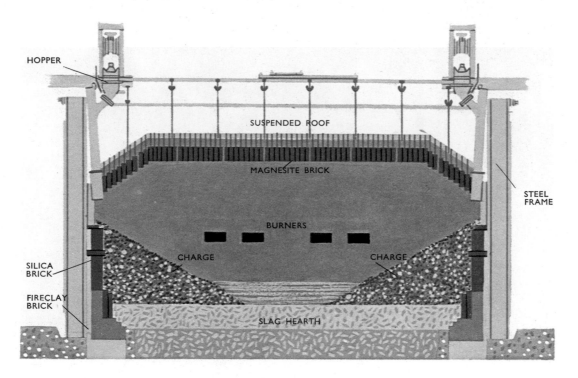

HOPPER

SUSPENDED ROOF

MAGNESITE BRICK

STEEL FRAME

BURNERS

CHARGE

CHARGE

SILICA BRICK

FIRECLAY BRICK

SLAG HEARTH

*Section of a smelting furnace.*

CHAPTER FIVE

# Refining Precious Metals

HOWEVER precious a metal may be, no one with an eye to business would go to the trouble and expense of digging thousands of tons of earth out of the ground and refining it just to recover one ounce of the metal. It simply would not be an economic proposition.

The ore of the Sudbury district of Canada is like this. The ore contains minute traces of precious metals, but it would never be mined for its precious metal content alone. Instead, it is mined for its nickel, copper and iron, in which it is extremely rich.

The first task after mining is to separate the particles containing metals from the useless earth or *gangue*. This is really done to concentrate the nickel, copper and iron, but it so happens that the precious metals are also concentrated, and stay with the nickel and copper instead of being removed. The extraction of nickel and copper continues and as more and more of the unwanted non-metals are removed, the concentration of the precious metals as impurities rises.

Silver and gold tend to stay with the copper and are separated from it only when the copper is finally purified by *electrolysis*. An anode made of the impure copper gradually dissolves and pure copper deposits itself on the cathode. As this happens, the silver, gold and other impurities that do not dissolve, drop to the bottom of the tank and form a slime there. This slime

31

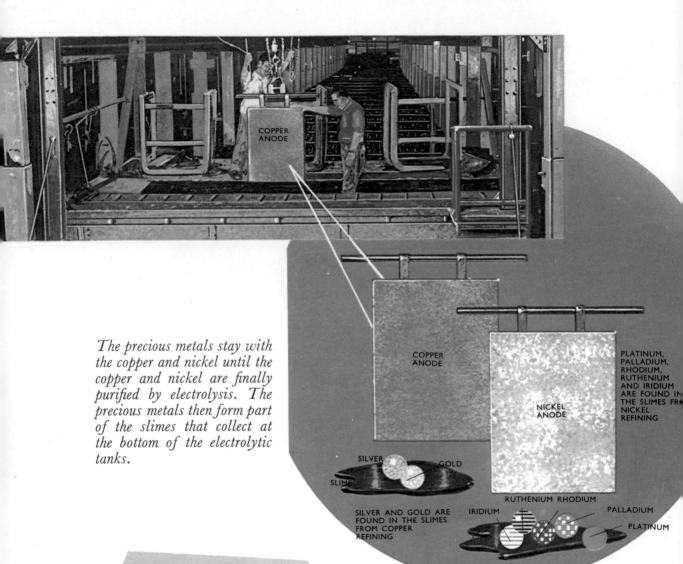

The precious metals stay with the copper and nickel until the copper and nickel are finally purified by electrolysis. The precious metals then form part of the slimes that collect at the bottom of the electrolytic tanks.

COPPER ANODE

NICKEL ANODE

PLATINUM, PALLADIUM, RHODIUM, RUTHENIUM AND IRIDIUM ARE FOUND IN THE SLIMES FROM NICKEL REFINING

SILVER

GOLD

SLIME

SILVER AND GOLD ARE FOUND IN THE SLIMES FROM COPPER REFINING

RUTHENIUM RHODIUM

IRIDIUM

PALLADIUM

PLATINUM

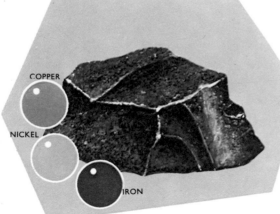

COPPER

NICKEL

IRON

*The ore of the Sudbury district of Canada is mined for its nickel, copper and iron. It also contains traces of precious metals.*

is so rich that it is well worth extracting the silver and gold from it. Because there are acres and acres of electrolytic tanks, the quantity of slime is quite considerable.

The larger group of precious metals, platinum and its chemical relatives, tends to stay with the nickel until it is finally purified. If the nickel is purified by electrolysis, the platinum metals are left in the slime from the anode. In the *Mond Carbonyl Process*, the nickel is wafted away as a gas (nickel carbonyl) and the precious metals are left behind.

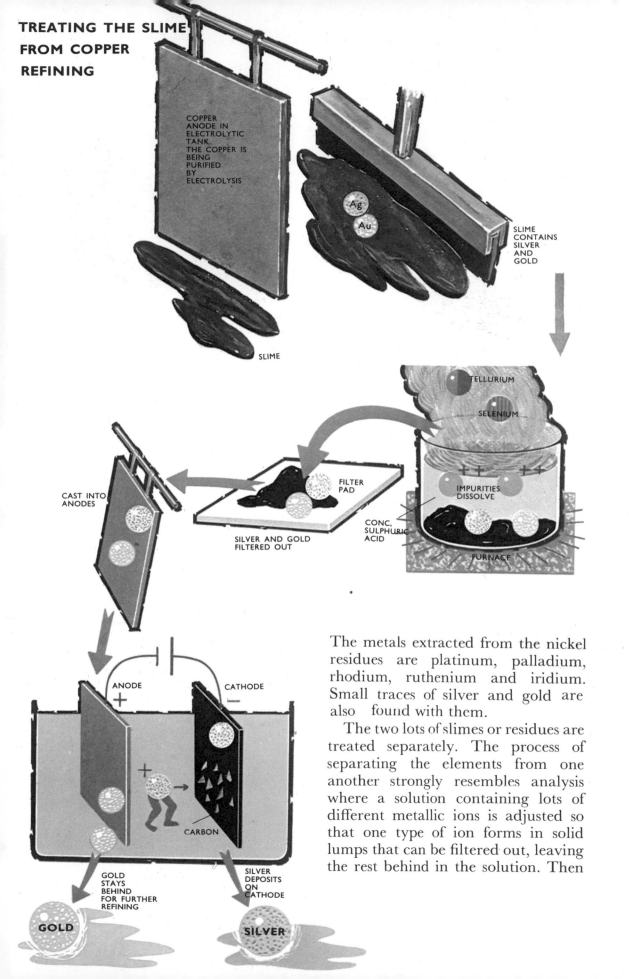

# TREATING THE SLIME FROM COPPER REFINING

COPPER ANODE IN ELECTROLYTIC TANK. THE COPPER IS BEING PURIFIED BY ELECTROLYSIS

SLIME

Ag
Au

SLIME CONTAINS SILVER AND GOLD

TELLURIUM

SELENIUM

IMPURITIES DISSOLVE

FILTER PAD

SILVER AND GOLD FILTERED OUT

CONC. SULPHURIC ACID

FURNACE

CAST INTO ANODES

ANODE
+

CATHODE

CARBON

GOLD STAYS BEHIND FOR FURTHER REFINING

SILVER DEPOSITS ON CATHODE

GOLD

SILVER

The metals extracted from the nickel residues are platinum, palladium, rhodium, ruthenium and iridium. Small traces of silver and gold are also found with them.

The two lots of slimes or residues are treated separately. The process of separating the elements from one another strongly resembles analysis where a solution containing lots of different metallic ions is adjusted so that one type of ion forms in solid lumps that can be filtered out, leaving the rest behind in the solution. Then

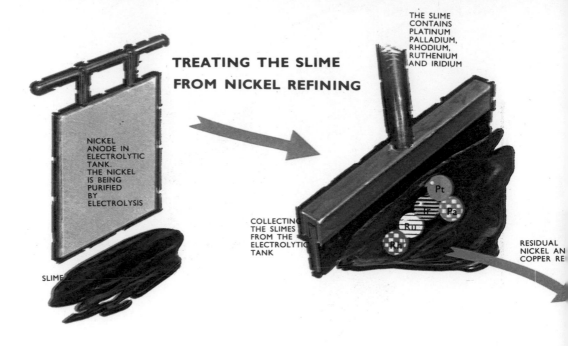

## TREATING THE SLIME FROM NICKEL REFINING

NICKEL ANODE IN ELECTROLYTIC TANK. THE NICKEL IS BEING PURIFIED BY ELECTROLYSIS

SLIME

THE SLIME CONTAINS PLATINUM PALLADIUM, RHODIUM, RUTHENIUM AND IRIDIUM

COLLECTING THE SLIMES FROM THE ELECTROLYTIC TANK

RESIDUAL NICKEL AN COPPER RE

Pt

Ir  Pa

Ru

Rh

the next metal can be removed in the same way. The jumbled mixture of ions swimming around in a solution is sorted out into heaps of solid compounds with each heap containing only one type of metallic ion.

In the precious metals refinery the elements are sorted out in much the same way, only on a much larger scale. Large vats replace the test tubes of the analytical laboratory and filter pads replace the filter funnels.

The brightly coloured precipitates, each one containing a different metal, receive individual treatment to convert them into the metal itself. Each metal is then purified in the way best suited to it.

## Treating the slime from copper refining

Concentrated sulphuric acid is added to the black slime and the container is heated up in a furnace. Copper and nickel in the slimes go into solution as sulphates, but the other metals, largely silver and gold, do not.

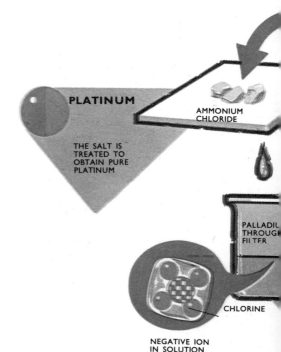

PLATINUM

AMMONIUM CHLORIDE

THE SALT IS TREATED TO OBTAIN PURE PLATINUM

PALLADI THROUGH FILTER

CHLORINE

NEGATIVE ION IN SOLUTION

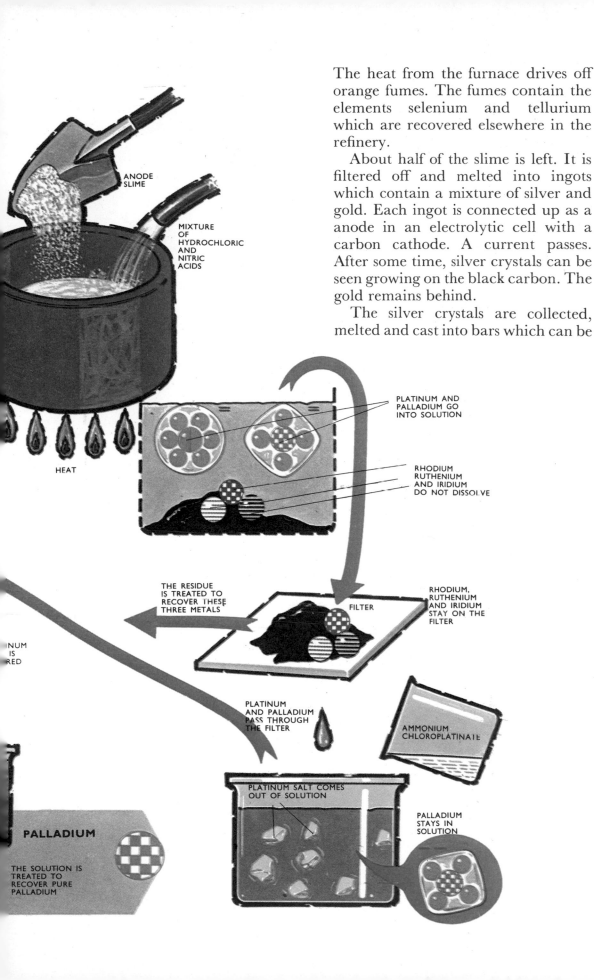

The heat from the furnace drives off orange fumes. The fumes contain the elements selenium and tellurium which are recovered elsewhere in the refinery.

About half of the slime is left. It is filtered off and melted into ingots which contain a mixture of silver and gold. Each ingot is connected up as a anode in an electrolytic cell with a carbon cathode. A current passes. After some time, silver crystals can be seen growing on the black carbon. The gold remains behind.

The silver crystals are collected, melted and cast into bars which can be

ANODE SLIME

MIXTURE OF HYDROCHLORIC AND NITRIC ACIDS

HEAT

PLATINUM AND PALLADIUM GO INTO SOLUTION

RHODIUM RUTHENIUM AND IRIDIUM DO NOT DISSOLVE

THE RESIDUE IS TREATED TO RECOVER THESE THREE METALS

FILTER

RHODIUM, RUTHENIUM AND IRIDIUM STAY ON THE FILTER

PLATINUM AND PALLADIUM PASS THROUGH THE FILTER

AMMONIUM CHLOROPLATINATE

PLATINUM SALT COMES OUT OF SOLUTION

PALLADIUM STAYS IN SOLUTION

PALLADIUM

THE SOLUTION IS TREATED TO RECOVER PURE PALLADIUM

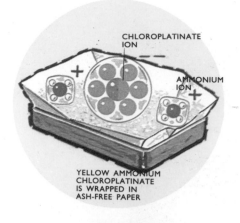

*Obtaining platinum metal from the yellow platinum salt. Heating drives off the ammonia and chlorine, leaving the metal behind.*

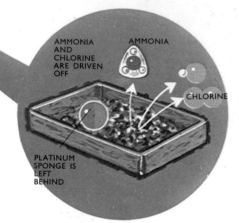

used for making jewellery or photographic papers and films.

The gold is gathered up but is not pure enough to be cast into ingots straight away. All this is dissolved and reagents are added so that only the gold is brought out of solution as a mustard coloured powder called gold sand. The impurities are left in the solution. The crude gold is melted, cast into anodes and refined electrolytically.

The platinum metals which remain in solution are treated with the slimes from the nickel refinery.

### Treating the slime from nickel refining

Three of the metals in the slime are dissolved so that they can be separated from the rest and brought out of solution one type at a time. This is done by heating the slimes with a mixture of concentrated hydrochloric and nitric acids in a steam-jacketed vat. Gold, platinum and palladium dissolve; rhodium, ruthenium and iridium do not. The insoluble particles are filtered out and the solution is treated, first of all to recover the gold, then the platinum and finally the palladium.

The gold comes out of a solution as a brown spongy metal when ferrous sulphate solution is added. After filtering out the spongy gold the platinum is brought down as brilliant orange-yellow particles of ammonium chloroplatinate when ammonium chloride solution is added. The platinum metal is extracted from this platinum salt by wrapping the salt up and burning it. The palladium is also brought out of solution as a salt.

The rhodium, iridium and ruthenium slime is then treated to separate these three metals.

All of the metals produced in this refinery have a great rarity value which makes it worthwhile extracting them in this fashion. All of them have a high resistance to heat and corrosion. Whereas other metals rust, corrode and crumble away, these metals stay bright and shiny. They are therefore very useful for jobs where corrosion must be avoided at all costs. Jewellery is an obvious example but the most important uses are industrial. Rhodium plated reflectors are used on searchlights. Rhodium is used for

electrical contacts; so are platinum and palladium. Spinnerets for extruding man-made fibres are made of platinum because it can stand up to both acidic and alkaline conditions and not wear out quickly. Platinum and rhodium are alloyed together for thermocouple wire. Platinum is used in the laboratory and to line glass melting crucibles.

Platinum and palladium are also used a great deal as catalysts to speed up chemical reactions. They will attract gas molecules onto their surfaces. As the molecules are brought closer together they have more chance of reacting with one another. It is often much more efficient to use platinum or palladium than to go to the trouble of compressing the gases under very high pressures.

CHAPTER SIX

# Aluminium

ALUMINIUM is a relative newcomer to the list of metals which man has put to his daily use. A hundred years ago it was so rare that it came in the same costly category as gold or silver – too expensive for practical things. At one time it could fetch a price of up to three pounds an ounce.

It was not until the 1880's that a way was found to produce aluminium cheaply and in quantity. A Frenchman, Paul Héroult, and an American, Charles Martin Hall, quite independently of each other, discovered the means of producing aluminium commercially by electrolysis (the chemical decomposition of a substance by the passage of an electric current through it). Today, aluminium ranks as the

most widely used non-ferrous metal in the world.

From this original method of producing aluminium has been developed the Bayer process, which is the most common method in use today. In this process, the aluminium ore (bauxite) is first crushed and washed to remove clay and any other unwanted matter. It is then further broken down and digested in hot caustic soda. At this stage the oxide of the bauxite is dissolved and soluble sodium aluminate is formed. A series of cleansing operations remove any further impurities, and the solution of aluminate is cooled. As it cools solid aluminium hydroxide is precipitated. The next step is to eliminate the water from the hydroxide crystals to obtain alumin-

*Molten aluminium is taken from the smelter and poured into moulds to form ingots weighing about 50 pounds.*

ium oxide (alumina). This process is known as calcination and is achieved simply by heating the aluminium hydroxide in long revolving drums. The final stage is extracting the aluminium from the alumina by electrolysis.

The alumina is placed in small 'furnaces', together with molten cryolite, another compound of aluminium, though not as common as bauxite. Alumina itself has a very high melting point of over 2,000°C but it will dissolve in molten cryolite (about 1,000°C) and the *solution* will allow the passage of a current of electricity through it. The 'furnace' is really a form of electrical cell, a steel bath with carbon lining to act as a cathode (negative plate) and other carbon blocks in contact with the liquid to form anodes (the positive connection). A strong current is passed through the mixture at about 6 volts, splitting up the substances electrically and generating great heat which maintains the temperature at 1,000°C. Molten aluminium is deposited at the cathode at the bottom of the furnace. From time to time it is drawn off and poured into ingot moulds. The gas which is liberated during electrolysis rises to come in contact with the red-hot carbon anodes to form carbon monoxide. This gas burns at the surface to form carbon dioxide which is led away as fumes.

The process of electrolysis consumes a huge quantity of electricity. It takes about 20,000 kilowatt-hours of electrical energy to process one ton of aluminium – enough electricity to serve the needs of an average home for ten years, or to keep a normal two-bar electric fire burning for 10,000 hours. Electric power, therefore, is an essential factor in producing low-priced aluminium. It is for this very reason that the location of an aluminium plant is tied to a source of electricity which is both plentiful and cheap.

Aluminium is the most abundant

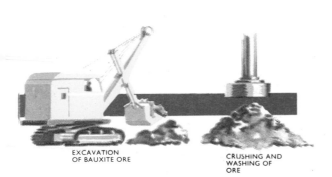

EXCAVATION OF BAUXITE ORE

CRUSHING AND WASHING OF ORE

**MAIN STAGES IN THE MANUFACTURE OF ALUMINIUM**

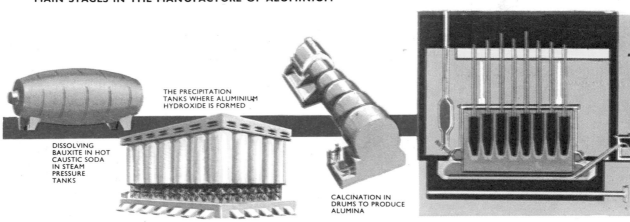

ELECTROLYTIC FURNACE

THE PRECIPITATION TANKS WHERE ALUMINIUM HYDROXIDE IS FORMED

DISSOLVING BAUXITE IN HOT CAUSTIC SODA IN STEAM PRESSURE TANKS

CALCINATION IN DRUMS TO PRODUCE ALUMINA

metal in the Earth's crust. The most common source of the metal is from the high-grade bauxite ore, yielding an aluminium content of over 60%. Bauxite deposits are formed by the decomposition, under moist tropical conditions, of clays and limestones. Thus, the largest deposits of bauxite are to be found in the tropical or near tropical areas of the earth (the fact that large deposits of bauxite occur in temperate regions in the U.S.A., France, Hungary and Russia is considered by geologists as evidence that a tropical climate existed many millions of years ago in those regions). From this fact, arises a second important factor in the location of the industry, that of transport. It is necessary for many of the industrialized countries to obtain the majority of their bauxite ore from the distant lands of the tropics. This means that aluminium plants, depending upon imported bauxite, must be located close to the coast or on a navigable river to keep costly overland transport to a minimum and thus ensure economic production.

These factors of production have led to some unusual sites for aluminium plants. In many cases, established industrial sites have not been suitable. One of the cheapest ways of producing electricity is by a water-powered generator (hydro-electric power) and since the greater the distance the electricity has to travel, the greater the cost involved, aluminium plants tend to be located as near to the source of electricity as possible. The famous Kitimat installations in Canada are a great distance from normal industrial areas. In the north-west of Canada, this plant is at the heart of the power source afforded by the abundant water power provided by the many local rivers. Similarly, in the Alps and Pyrenees in Europe, hydro-electricity has attracted a number of aluminium plants.

Other cheap methods of producing electricity are being developed, notably the use of natural gas, but most aluminium plants still rely upon electricity supplies from hydro-electric stations.

# Physical
# Metallurgy

# CHAPTER SEVEN

# Metals are Made of Crystals

THE pattern of a mosaic floor always remains clear and distinct no matter how much it is polished and worn smooth. There are always markings showing where one marble tile stops and the next one begins. These boundaries are easy to see even when the neighbouring blocks are of the same colour.

As a piece of metal is made up of lots of crystals, like the blocks of marble in the mosaic, the surface of the metal too would be expected to take on the appearance of a mosaic and be covered with a lattice work of patterning wherever one crystal borders onto another one.

But this is very rarely seen. Most pieces of metal do not look as though they are made up of small crystals. A polished silver teapot has a radiant sheen, but there are no markings on its surface to show that it is crystalline. Crystals are usually only seen jutting out of the edge of a piece of metal when the metal has been snapped in two.

Because of this, many people wrongly believe that the metals are normally quite even and smooth throughout – rather like a very rigid slab of butter – and definitely non-crystalline, and that for some strange reason an internal change could take place making the metal brittle, so that the metal crystallizes, becomes weak and breaks.

There is, in fact, no foundation at all for this idea. All solid metals and metallic mixtures are crystalline by nature. The crystalline nature is not a sign of weakness. Some forces acting on the metal must have made it snap along the boundaries between crystals.

*Pouring molten metal into a mould to make a sand casting. The cast metal will later be polished, etched and examined microscopically.*

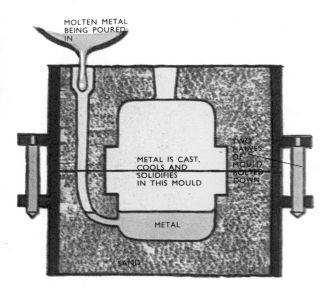

MOLTEN METAL BEING POURED IN

METAL IS CAST, COOLS AND SOLIDIFIES IN THIS MOULD

TWO HALVES OF MOULD BOLTED DOWN

METAL

SAND

*Cross section of a sand casting mould.*

surface of a polished silver teapot.

However, if the surface layer is etched away the small crystals can be seen clearly by examination under an ordinary microscope or, if they are very small, under an electron microscope. First of all, some molten metal is allowed to cool and solidify in a crucible. Then, when it is cold, a piece of metal is cut off and polished with fine abrasive till it shines like a mirror.

*Viewing an etched metal surface. Because light is reflected differently by each grain surface, the different grains show up by contrast.*

If the crystals of metal happen to be large enough, reflections from the exposed crystal faces can be seen. This sort of breakage is known as '*inter-crystalline*' *failure*. It is rather like breaking a mosaic pattern.

The small blocks from which the mosaic is made usually remain intact. Only the pattern is broken as the mosaic shatters at the joints between the blocks. The same thing happens when a brittle piece of metal snaps in two. The crystals remain intact but the structure shatters at the boundaries between the crystals. More often, though, when a metal fractures, the crystals themselves break. This is known as '*transcrystalline*' *failure*.

Usually crystals of metal are far too small to be seen with the naked eye. Also, when a metal is polished the surface structure is spoiled and the metal atoms are spread over the surface rather like butter being spread over a slice of bread. This is the reason there are no crystals to be seen in the

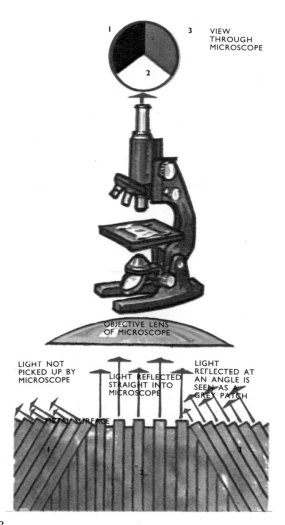

VIEW THROUGH MICROSCOPE

OBJECTIVE LENS OF MICROSCOPE

LIGHT NOT PICKED UP BY MICROSCOPE

LIGHT REFLECTED STRAIGHT INTO MICROSCOPE

LIGHT REFLECTED AT AN ANGLE IS SEEN AS A GREY PATCH

METAL SURFACE

43

The mirror finish is then dissolved away with a suitable chemical reagent. The crystals are attacked and the surface after etching is no longer flat. The different surfaces then reflect light in different directions causing a contrast. The pattern can be seen quite clearly with the microscope.

The metal consists of a *matrix* or mass of metallic grains. Because the solid sample has been cast or poured as a liquid into a mould and allowed to set, the structure revealed by the microscope is known as the '*as cast*' structure.

This crystalline structure is one of the most important factors in the behaviour of the metal and anything done to affect that structure, such as rolling the metal or heating it in a furnace, will affect most of its other physical properties.

The liquid metal consists of a mass of metal atoms all moving about independently, without any relation to each other. As the metal cools to its freezing point, tiny specks of solid, called *nuclei* appear here and there

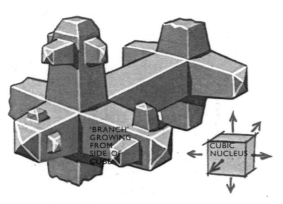

Branches of a dendrite growing out from the sides of a cubic nucleus.

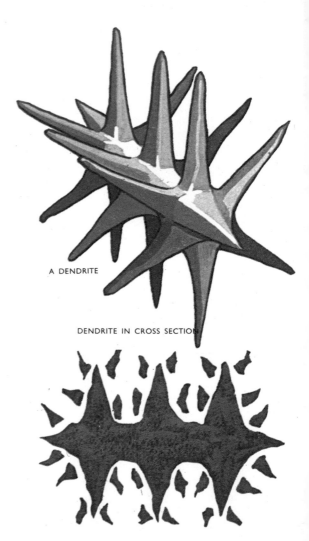

A DENDRITE

DENDRITE IN CROSS SECTION

*Dendrites seen in the surface of some cast antimony (twice life size).*

*Diagram and cross section of a dendrite.*

44

throughout the liquid. These are small groups of atoms. There is no sort of order about where they start to form in the liquid, they are just scattered around in it.

At the instant of joining together these atoms give up their independence. They are no longer free to wander through the liquid as they wish, but have to remain near to the rest of the group.

A three-dimensional framework or *crystal lattice* is building up. This lattice is different for each different metal and is made up of the metal atoms in a regular geometric array. As the metal loses heat, more and more atoms give up their freedom of movement in the liquid to attach themselves to a nucleus. The pattern around the nuclei grows bigger and bigger as more of the liquid solidifies.

In a cooling liquid metal this process takes place simultaneously at a number of points and each little lattice block so formed grows out to meet its neighbours.

The atoms do not just build up on the nuclei in cubes or blocks, but usually grow up into structures like pine trees, called *dendrites*. Even if the starting nucleus is a cube-shaped cluster of atoms, the cube will cool less quickly at the corners than in the centre. Because of this, growth takes place on the faces and then again on the faces of the new tiny cubes deposited there. This promotes a spiky growth.

Eventually the dendrites grow until they are obstructed from further growth by collision with their neighbours. The remaining liquid solidifies in the space between them and a solid structure is formed.

Because all the nuclei have started at different angles to each other the crystals also have grown at different angles to each other, and the metal does not solidify as one large crystal but as lots of small ones. The boundaries where these 'crystals' meet are not symmetrical. The tiny crystals are usually referred to as *grains* because they have different shapes. The boundaries are then called *grain boundaries*.

So, each grain in the solid metal has grown from a single dendrite and all the atoms in that grain are arranged uniformly. Neighbouring grains have the same basic atomic or lattice pattern, but they are tilted towards each other at all sorts of different angles.

# CHAPTER EIGHT

# Metallic Strength and Dislocations

IT is possible to work out how strong a piece of metal should be from the way its atoms are arranged and from the forces acting between the various atoms. This gives the *theoretical strength* of the metal.

The theoretical strength and the strength found by actual measurement are two very different values. Metals in practice show a strength much lower than their theoretical

*To break a piece of metal, the lattice must be broken. There are two ways of doing this. The atomic layers can be pulled apart as they are here or they can be slid one over another.*

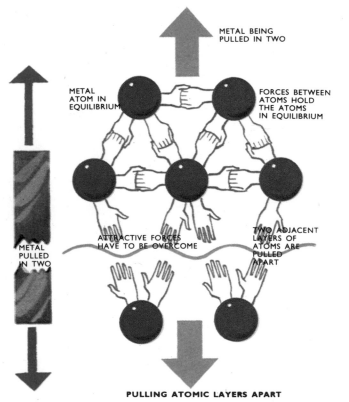

METAL BEING
PULLED IN TWO

METAL
ATOM IN
EQUILIBRIUM

FORCES BETWEEN
ATOMS HOLD
THE ATOMS
IN EQUILIBRIUM

ATTRACTIVE FORCES
HAVE TO BE OVERCOME

TWO ADJACENT
LAYERS OF
ATOMS ARE
PULLED
APART

METAL
PULLED
IN TWO

**PULLING ATOMIC LAYERS APART**

strength. This difference is considerable. Theoretical values can be as much as *1,000 times greater* than the normal strength found in any metal. The implications of these shortcomings are obvious. If metals behave in the theoretical manner, components in engineering and construction work would need to be only a fraction of the size, with all the accompanying saving in space, weight and cost.

What causes this discrepancy in strength values? To find out, it is best to consider in detail what happens when a *metal* is fractured. Metals normally consist of an aggregate of *crystals* or *grains*. Within these grains the metallic atoms are arranged in a regular geometric pattern, or *lattice*. This lattice may be thought of as a three dimensional array of planes of atoms, with all atoms approximately equally spaced from their neighbours. *The atoms maintain their positions in space due to a balance between the attractive and repulsive forces acting on them.* Anything trying to disturb that equilibrium, trying to deform the lattice, meets strong resistance. This gives the metal its characteristic strength.

A single metal crystal can be fractured by separating two of the planes of atoms with a straight pull at right angles to them. The total force needed will be the sum of all the attractive forces between the atoms in one plane and their opposite numbers in the adjacent plane. This force, which can be calculated, gives the maximum stress which any given metal could *theoretically* withstand. But, even in a single

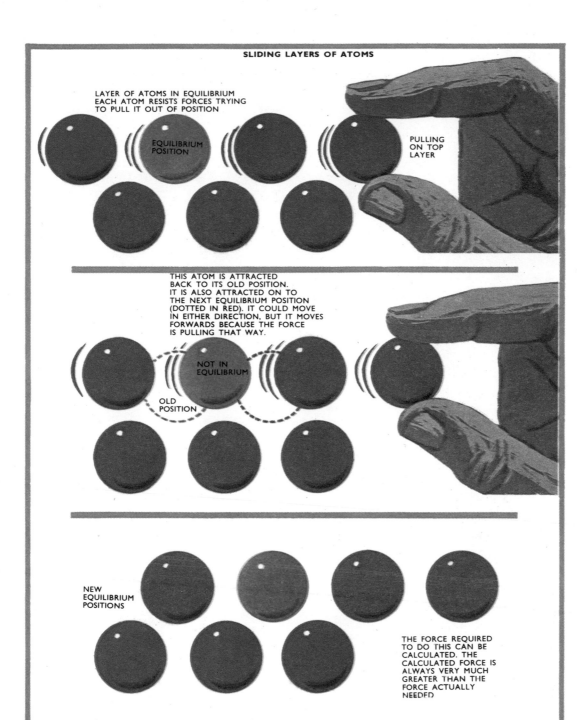

LAYER OF ATOMS IN EQUILIBRIUM
EACH ATOM RESISTS FORCES TRYING
TO PULL IT OUT OF POSITION

EQUILIBRIUM
POSITION

PULLING
ON TOP
LAYER

THIS ATOM IS ATTRACTED
BACK TO ITS OLD POSITION.
IT IS ALSO ATTRACTED ON TO
THE NEXT EQUILIBRIUM POSITION
(DOTTED IN RED). IT COULD MOVE
IN EITHER DIRECTION, BUT IT MOVES
FORWARDS BECAUSE THE FORCE
IS PULLING THAT WAY.

NOT IN
EQUILIBRIUM

OLD
POSITION

NEW
EQUILIBRIUM
POSITIONS

THE FORCE REQUIRED
TO DO THIS CAN BE
CALCULATED. THE
CALCULATED FORCE IS
ALWAYS VERY MUCH
GREATER THAN THE
FORCE ACTUALLY
NEEDED

The forces calculated to break a piece of metal by pulling the atomic layers apart or sliding the layers of atoms one over the other are much greater than those found in practice. In other words, the metal is much weaker than it theoretically should be.

crystal, it is impossible to ensure even distribution of the stress over the cleavage plane, and local concentrations of stress may be expected to lower the strength. If there were no stress concentrations, the theoretical strength would be about 1,000 times that of the normal strength for a metal. Even allowing for the stress concentrations, the strength should still be several hundred times greater than is observed. However, a piece of metal normally consists of more than one crystal. In a metal, the atomic planes in the crystals are not aligned with each other and so cannot respond uniformly to an applied stress. This gives rise to stress concentrations. The boundaries between grains of metal, where the lattice breaks down completely, have a similar effect. Even so, this does not account for all the weakness of the metal.

There is another way of fracturing a piece of metal. A *shear force* can be used to *slide* a plane of atoms across another. When a force is applied to slide one plane over another, there is, of course, resistance. However, when a particular atom has moved about halfway from its old stable position it begins to be attracted to a new stable position that is now being vacated. As the atom will be in equilibrium in either position and it is being pulled forward, it goes forward, *helping* the external shear force. This process will continue as long as the shear force is applied. The lattice, the crystals and in turn the whole piece of metal is therefore deformed.

This state of affairs, where the atoms move permanently to a new

*Making dislocation-free silicon by slowly withdrawing a crystal that is just dipping in some molten silicon. The crystal grows as it is pulled out. This silicon is much stronger than ordinary silicon.*

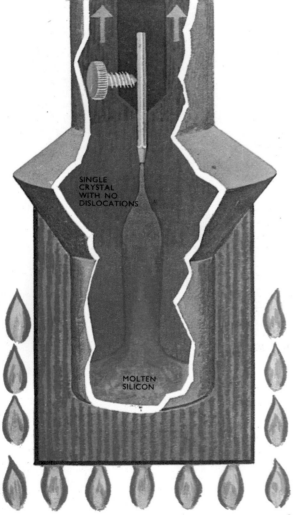

SINGLE CRYSTAL WITH NO DISLOCATIONS

MOLTEN SILICON

*A spiral growth, point of weakness which formed when some paraffin wax cooled.*

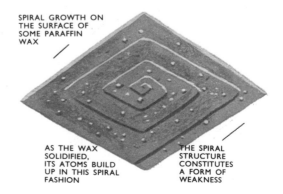

SPIRAL GROWTH ON THE SURFACE OF SOME PARAFFIN WAX

AS THE WAX SOLIDIFIED, ITS ATOMS BUILD UP IN THIS SPIRAL FASHION

THE SPIRAL STRUCTURE CONSTITUTES A FORM OF WEAKNESS

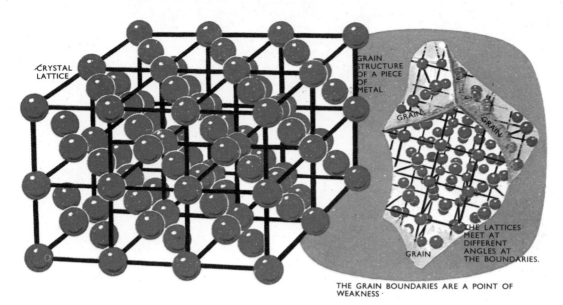

CRYSTAL LATTICE

GRAIN STRUCTURE OF A PIECE OF METAL

GRAIN

GRAIN

GRAIN

THE LATTICES MEET AT DIFFERENT ANGLES AT THE BOUNDARIES.

THE GRAIN BOUNDARIES ARE A POINT OF WEAKNESS.

*Metal atoms in grains of metal are arranged in a lattice. Forces binding the atoms together make it difficult to part them.*

position and give a permanent deformation to the metal, is called *plastic deformation*. If, on the other hand, when the deforming force is released, the atoms spring back to their *original* positions, only *elastic* deformation has taken place. If the shearing is taken to its limit, the metal will fail or fracture. So this is another mechanism of failure. But does this account for the low observed strengths? The answer is 'No'. Even failure by pure shear gives theoretical results several hundred times greater than the real strength of the metal.

A lump of metal does not behave uniformly throughout. The metal is more likely to crack in some places than others.

The boundary between grains of metal is probably the weakest part of the system, but, except under special circumstances, is unlikely to fail.

The atomic planes are held together by the strongest forces and cleavage is unlikely to occur. If it did, however, there would be considerable elastic, but no plastic deformation.

Intermediate in strength is the shear strength of the atomic layers. These layers are the most likely to fail, again with considerable elastic, and little plastic, deformation. However, it is obvious that the theory does not agree with the practice. Very pure metals show almost no elasticity and unlimited plasticity. From theoretical reasoning it should be the other way round. A piece of gold for example, may be beaten to a foil thin enough to transmit light.

It would seem then, that the theory is wrong. But, there is evidence to support it and with carefully controlled conditions, theoretical results can be approached. Whiskers of metal that have very high strengths have been made in the laboratory. Iron, for instance, has been made with breaking stresses of about 850 tons per square inch compared with a normal figure of about 22 tons per square inch. In view of this it is obvious that there is some influence operating on ordinary metal crystals, which weakens them and which prevents them behaving in the

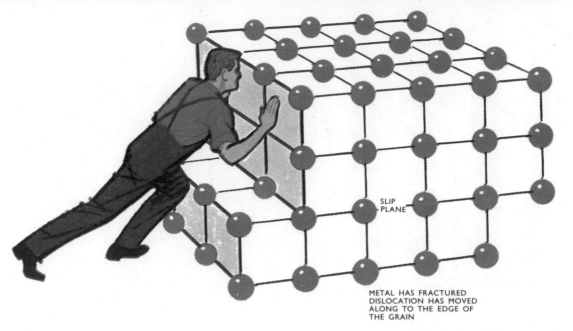

SLIP PLANE

METAL HAS FRACTURED
DISLOCATION HAS MOVED
ALONG TO THE EDGE OF
THE GRAIN

*Minute screw-shaped patterns can be seen in the surface of some metals. They indicate another source of weakness, the screw dislocation.*

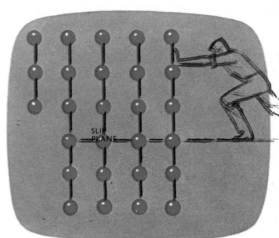

SLIP PLANE

*Lattice containing a screw dislocation. The dislocation travels along a slip plane to the end of the grain, helping the metal to fracture.*

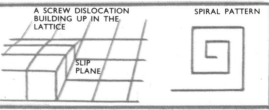

A SCREW DISLOCATION
BUILDING UP IN THE
LATTICE

SLIP
PLANE

SPIRAL PATTERN

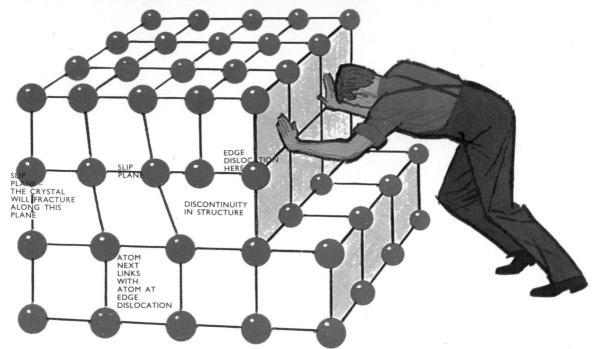

*An edge dislocation, a point of weakness in a piece of metal. One atomic plane is not complete and the metal can fail much more easily because of this. When one layer of atoms is pushed over another the dislocation acts as a stepping stone making the process easier.*

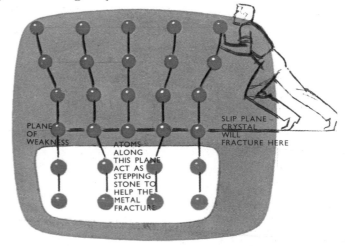

theoretical manner. Only in recent years has the explanation become clear. The solution lies in the fact that crystals rarely exist in the perfect form and the lattices contain defects of different kinds. A particular defect has been proved to exist in structures and it has properties which make the metal much weaker. This defect is called a *dislocation* and, as its name implies, arises from a misplacement of the atomic bonds in part of the plane of a crystal.

CHAPTER NINE

# Alloys

IT is no use purifying a metal in the hope that it will become stronger. Most pure metals are soft and do not have much mechanical strength. They would be far too weak for the majority of engineering purposes. Pure iron is extremely weak and railway bridges and girders made from it would quickly collapse.

Weakness and brittleness tend to characterize any metal which has been *cast* by pouring it into a mould and allowing it to set. Metals cast in this fashion can be strengthened by some form of mechanical treatment like hammering and rolling. Although it helps, even rolling and forging a really pure metal does not give sufficient hardness and strength to be of any real use.

Most metals are therefore not used in their pure form, but are mixed with other metals to form *alloys*. There can be two, three, four or any number of different metals in a single alloy. The *binary alloys*, made by mixing two molten metals together, are naturally the simplest alloys to understand.

The number of possible alloys is enormous because most combinations of metals will mingle together and alloy satisfactorily. Just a few will not. Not all of these alloys are improvements on the original pure metal. Sometimes the original metal is worsened by additions. Adding a small amount of the metal bismuth to copper only makes it brittle and useless. The bismuth forms a tiny weak envelope around each copper grain and when any stress is applied, the copper breaks and shatters at the boundaries between the grains.

The alloys that are improvements find their way into common use and the others are rejected.

Though pure iron itself is extremely weak, there is an enormous range of strong, iron-containing alloys. The simplest of these alloys (almost all are called *steels*) contains only iron and carbon. The proportion of carbon varies between 0.05% in *wrought iron* to 4.5% in *cast iron*. By careful choice of the ratio of carbon to iron, a steel can be made which is suitable for almost any purpose. In addition to these alloys, a number of more complex steels are produced for special purposes. For instance *tungsten steel*, containing comparatively

*An alloy is a mixture of two or more metals. Alloys consisting of two metals only are called binary alloys.*

small amounts of tungsten, chromium and carbon in the iron, is used for making the cutting edges of tools, particularly those which are operated at high speeds.

Aluminium alloys have proved very useful in the aircraft industry where a high strength is required from a very light-weight alloy. Many of

*Most alloys are stronger than the parent metal, but some are much weaker. Bismuth greatly weakens copper because it forms a brittle envelope around each copper grain.*

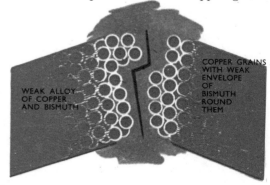

To form an alloy, two or more metals must mingle together. As there are several different ways in which this can happen, there must also be several different types of alloy.

Two molten metals can be absolutely soluble in one another, with the atoms of each metal free to wander around in the solution just like the atoms and molecules in any other true solution.

When a mixture like this solidifies, two different things can happen. In one type of alloy, the two metals remain completely dissolved in one another. Examination under a microscope shows the same type of crystal throughout the alloy and no trace of any crystals of either of the pure metals. This is complete solid solubility and the alloy is a *one phase alloy*.

On solidification the two metals may be only partially soluble in one another. The solid alloy is made up of two different types of crystal. One type consists largely of one metal with a little of the other dissolved in it, while the other type of crystal consists largely of the other metal. This is a *two phase alloy* and is probably the most common type.

When the two metals are insoluble in one another, crystals of one of the pure metals are embedded in a finely dispersed metallic mixture.

## THREE WAYS IN WHICH METALS CAN MIX

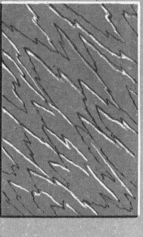

Complete solid solubility. One metal has dissolved completely in another. There is no trace of crystals of either of the pure metals.

Partial solubility. A two phase structure. Most alloys are of this type. Crystals of one composition are embedded in crystals of another.

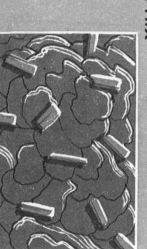

Two metals are insoluble. Crystals of one pure metal are embedded in the other.

53

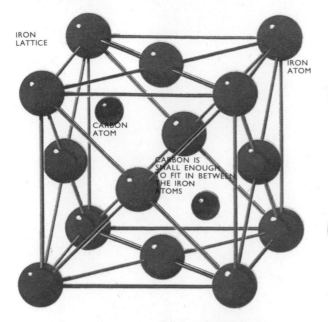

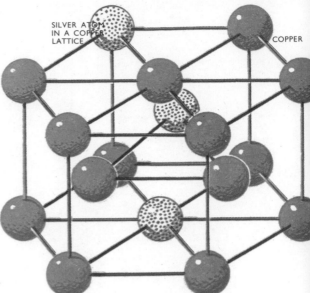

*Steel, an interstitial solid solution. Carbon atoms are small and manage to squeeze in the gaps between the atoms in the iron lattice.*

*Substitutional solid solution copper and silver atoms are about the same size. Silver atoms can take the place of copper in a copper lattice.*

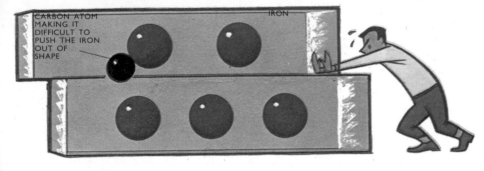

*The carbon impurity has strengthened the iron. It is now more difficult to push one atomic plane over another.*

## Solid Solutions

There are two types of solid solution depending on the relative sizes of the metal atoms involved.

In a *substitutional* solid solution the two types of metal have atoms that are about the same size. A foreign atom can take a place in a lattice structure without too much distortion of the lattice.

In an *interstitial* solid solution the foreign atoms are very much smaller and do not take up a place in the lattice. Instead, they squeeze into the gaps or interstices. Carbon and hydrogen with their small atoms can do this very well. Steel is an interstitial solid solution with atoms of carbon fitting in the gaps between iron atoms.

these aircraft alloys are made suitable for use by a special process known as *precipitation hardening*.

Stainless steel is one alloy which has become very popular because of its resistance to corrosion. It consists largely of iron alloyed with a high proportion of the metal, chromium. The chromium present forms a tough oxide layer on the surface of the steel which prevents the iron beneath from being corroded by the atmo-

## Solder

The ability to alter the range over which an alloy freezes by changing the composition is used in soft solders. These are lead/tin alloys. The 'tinmans solder' is an eutectic alloy. It is a rapid melting and a rapid freezing alloy. The soldered parts do not hold in place while the alloy freezes.

On the other hand, plumber's solder is chosen to have a wide freezing range in order that the joint may be 'wiped' to ensure soundness while the metal is still in the pasty stage of freezing.

THE GALVANIZED IRON PIPE AND BATH HAVE BEEN SOLDERED WITH A TIN/LEAD ALLOY

## Eutectics

Alloys that show little or no solubility often form what is called a eutectic. Here, the two metals concerned have the effect of lowering each other's melting points. Ultimately at one specific composition the alloy solidifies at a single composition as if it were a pure metal. This is called the eutectic point. Here an instantaneous transformation from liquid to solid takes place.

At all other compositions the alloy displays the normal solidifying behaviour and freezes over a range of temperatures.

## Simple Steels

| ALLOY | CARBON CONTENT (PER CENT) | PROPERTIES | TYPICAL USES |
|---|---|---|---|
| Wrought Iron | 0·05–0·15 | Ductile | Chains, bolts |
| Mild Steel | 0·1–0·25 | Strong | Girders, shafts |
| Medium Carbon Steel | 0·25–0·6 | Can be hardened | Agricultural tools |
| High Carbon Steel | 0·6–1·2 | Strong hard | Cutting tools |
| Very High Carbon Steel | over 1·2 | Extra hard | Drill bits |
| Cast Iron | 1·7–4·5 | Brittle, strong in compression | Machine bodies, columns. |


## Complex Alloy Steels

| ALLOY | CARBON CONTENT (PER CENT) | OTHER SUBSTANCES (PER CENT) | PROPERTIES | TYPICAL USES |
|---|---|---|---|---|
| Chrome-vanadium steel | 0·3 | Chromium 1·0; Vanadium 0·2 | Wear and shock resistant | Axles, gears |
| Invar | 0·2 | Nickel 36·0 | Very low co-efficient of expansion | Standards of length, accurate instruments |
| Manganese steel | 1·0 | Manganese 12·0 | Hard wearing, ductile | Armour plate, excavator buckets. |
| Nickel steel | 0·3 | Nickel 3·0 | Strong, hard, shock resistant | Gears, forgings |
| Nickel-chrome steel | 0·3 | Nickel 3·0; Chromium 1·0 | Hard wearing, ductile | Gears, crankshafts |
| Silicon steel | 0·1 | Silicon 2·0 | Good electromagnetic properties | Transformer cores |
| Silicon-manganese steel | 0·6 | Silicon 1·5; Manganese 0·6 | Resists fatigue | Springs, bridges. |
| Stainless steel | 0·3 | Chromium 18·0; Nickel 8·0 | Corrosion resist-ant, strong | Surgical instruments, chemical plant. |
| Tungsten steel | 0·7 | Tungsten 14·0; Chromium 4·0 | Hard, even when red hot | High speed cutting tools |

## Common Non-Ferrous Alloys

| ALLOY | TYPICAL COMPOSITION (PER CENT) | PROPERTIES | USES |
|---|---|---|---|
| Brass | Copper 60·0; Zinc 40·0 | Corrosion resistant | Bearings, castings |
| Bronze | Copper 90·0; Tin 10·0 | Corrosion resistant, good for casting | Castings |
| Constantan | Copper 55·0; Nickel 45·0 | Good electrical resistance, serves well when hot | Thermocouples |
| Cupronickel | Copper 75·0; Nickel 25·0 | Ductile, corrosion resistant | 'Silver' coins, turbine blades |
| Duralumin | Aluminium 95·0; Copper 4·0; Plus magnesium, manganese, iron and silicon | Light in weight, strong and corrosion resistant | Aircraft parts |
| German silver | Copper 50·0 Zinc 30·0; Nickel 20·0 | Corrosion resistant | Ornaments, car trimmings |
| Gun metal | Copper 88·0; Tin 10·0; Zinc 2·0 | Resists corrosion and wear | Castings |
| Phosphor bronze | Copper 88·0; Tin 9·7; Zinc 2·0; Phosphorus 0·3 | Corrosion resistant, hard but softens when heated | Bearing brushes, worm wheels |
| Solder | Tin 50·0; Lead 50·0 | Low melting point, seals well | Joining pieces of tin plate |
| White metal | Lead 64·0; Tin 20·0; Antimony 15·0; Copper 1·0 | Low melting point, low frictional resistance | Bearings |

sphere. Whenever the surface of the steel becomes scratched, the newly exposed chromium quickly oxidizes to form a fresh protective layer, and the steel stays bright and shiny.

There are three steps in deciding which metal or alloy should be used for making a particular part. First the designer notices the factors which are likely to cause failure in the part. He must ask himself: 'Is it going to work at a high temperature, or at varying temperatures? What forces will be acting upon it? Is it going to be subject to excessive wear, or to corrosive materials?'

When he has answered these questions the designer has reached the second stage – he can deduce the properties required of the material. Perhaps it will have to retain its strength over a wide range of temperature. Other parts need good resistance to wear. Then, once the designer knows what properties the material will need, he comes to the third stage and finds an alloy which is best suited to these requirements.

The accompanying tables give details of some of the more important alloys used in scientific instruments, and in engineering generally. The composition of some of the alloys described varies between quite wide limits and the figures quoted are average values only.

# CHAPTER TEN

# The Working Properties of Metals

WHY will some metals fold easily while others crack? Why will some stretch while others break? It is simply because different metals have different *properties* which the engineer must know about if he is to work them without spoiling them. The *properties* of metals means the ways in which they behave when subjected to forces or pressures. Workshop processes (such as cutting, bending, folding, stretching) are essentially ways of using forces or pressures to bring materials to the desired shape.

**Strength**

Strength is the measure of the amount of weight or load which a metal will carry. There are three main ways of loading a metal each of which may cause it to fail. They are called tension, compression and shear.

The maximum load which a bar will carry varies with the area of its cross-section. Hence the maximum load carried by a bar is not in itself enough to explain the strength of the

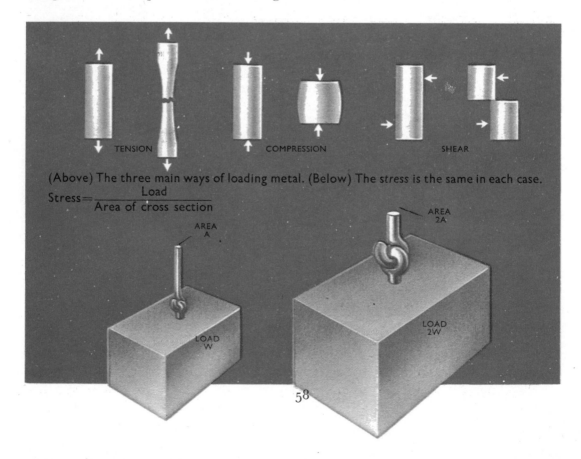

(Above) The three main ways of loading metal. (Below) The *stress* is the same in each case.

$$\text{Stress} = \frac{\text{Load}}{\text{Area of cross section}}$$

metal. The best way of measuring strength is to divide the load by the area of metal to find out what each unit of area will support.

$$\frac{\text{load (tons)}}{\text{cross-sectional area (sq. in.)}}$$
$$= \text{STRESS (tons per sq. in.)}$$

The biggest stress which a metal will carry before it breaks is called the *Ultimate Strength*. Mild steel, one of the most common metals, has an ultimate strength of about 25 tons per square inch. Alloy steels may have values as high as 100 tons per square inch. If the strength of a metal is known it is possible to calculate how much load any piece will carry. Thus a 75-ton locomotive could be supported by a bar of alloy steel $-\frac{75}{100} = \frac{3}{4}$ sq. in. area or roughly 1 in. diameter if in rod form.

Strong metals like this are hard to work. They take more force and energy and need heavy machines to do the bending and forming. Cutting tools absorb more power and do not last as long as when cutting weaker metals. Thus strong metals are expensive and cost more to work.

**Ductility**

If a metal is pulled it behaves just like a piece of elastic, except that the stretch is very small. This allows metal to be made into springs (a spring returns to the same position no matter how often it is used). This *elasticity* can be very troublesome in workshop operations because the metal cannot easily be bent into a new shape. Sometimes the metal is softened by heating, then bent, and afterwards heat-treated to regain its springiness.

But if a metal is stretched too far it becomes *plastic* and will extend permanently like putty. A metal bar stretched by a small stress will regain

*Testing the tensile strength of a metal. The sample is stretched and at each stage the stretching force (load) and the extensions (elongations) produced are recorded.*

its original shape when the stress is removed. But if the stress exceeds a certain value (called the Yield Stress) the bar will be permanently deformed. If the stress is increased further, the bar continues to stretch until (at the Ultimate Stress) it breaks.

Metals which stretch a lot when pulled are said to be *ductile*. By stretching a bar in a testing machine the elongation over a given length (called the gauge length) can be found. The percentage elongation of

59

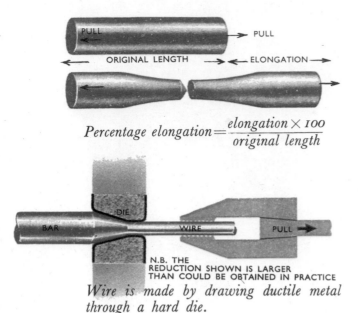

$$\text{Percentage elongation} = \frac{elongation \times 100}{original\ length}$$

*Wire is made by drawing ductile metal through a hard die.*

N.B. THE
REDUCTION SHOWN IS LARGER
THAN COULD BE OBTAINED IN PRACTICE

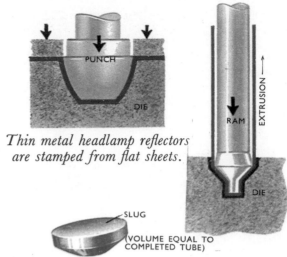

*Thin metal headlamp reflectors are stamped from flat sheets.*

*Making hollow tubes by extrusion.*

mild steel is 15 to 20%, of soft brass 30%, and of pure aluminium 40%. Most of the elongation takes place between the Yield Stress and the Ultimate Stress. Some metals stretch a lot, they have high ductility, and can be easily deformed by metal working processes, especially if they have a low tensile strength (resistance to stretching forces). This allows thin cases, such as car headlamp reflectors, to be formed (see diagram) from a flat sheet, sometimes with a single blow of the punch. This is, of course, much quicker and cheaper than forming by hand.

Wire is made by pulling a bar of ductile metal through a highly polished hole in a hard metal die which squeezes it into a smaller diameter— the smaller the diameter, the greater the length. Copper, which is very ductile, can be easily drawn into wire as thin as a hair. Even hollow tubes, almost as fine as hairs, can be made by this method. Steel bar can also be drawn, but only with difficulty and a little at a time because it is less ductile than copper. Even in this operation the *strength* of the metal is important, for if too great a reduction

in diameter is attempted the bar will break.

Drawn bar or wire has a smooth, accurate finish because it is polished by contact with the hard die. It is usually round and quite free from surface defects. It is therefore called bright drawn bar and is an important form of material because it can be used for many purposes without any further machining. When drawing or otherwise deforming a metal when it is cold, the crystal structure of the metal is distorted, causing the metal to stiffen. Consequently any bright metal bar or sheet (which is often cold-rolled) may be difficult to bend without cracking. If necessary, metal can be *annealed* (*i.e.* heated and then cooled very slowly) to soften it without losing its finish or accuracy. The engineer must know exactly the condition of the metal being used and must be careful to specify the right quality.

### Plasticity

Most people have used modelling clay for making models and know that it can be pushed into almost any shape. Many metals will behave in much the same way if stressed heavily enough, and can be forced into an entirely new shape. They are said to be *plastic*. In fact metal can be squirted, and this is done in a process known as *impact extrusion* which is used to make canisters, toothpaste tubes, and other thin-walled containers.

A slug of metal is put into a shallow hole in a solid metal die (see diagram). A ram then descends upon the slug with great force and compresses it within the hole. Due to the pressure, the metal becomes plastic and can only escape through the narrow space between the ram and the die cavity. The metal is squirted upwards through this space to form a thin-walled tube. All this happens in one second or less and so the process has a high output. Metals such as pure aluminium are very suitable indeed for this kind of process.

All ductile metals permit plastic flow, but some metals, such as lead, are soft and can be deformed, yet they are not ductile. These can be rolled and hammered and are called *malleable* metals. Aluminium is both malleable and ductile, and can be hammered or rolled into foil less than a thousandth of an inch thick. The 'tinfoil' used in the packing of cigarettes is actually aluminium foil.

Many metals become plastic when red-hot although they are not so when cold. Steel is easy to deform at a red heat. Most steel bars and plates are originally hot-rolled to size. Forging, another hot-working process, can form steel into almost any shape. Large changes in section can be made with relatively small forces, and this is the great advantage of forging. Also, the metal crystals do not stiffen, so that hot-worked metal remains soft and easy to bend. The combined effect of contraction on cooling and surface oxidation causes inaccuracy and discoloration and this is a disadvantage of hot working. Consequently we have to pay for easy plastic forming by much more machining, and this is another reason for choosing metals carefully.

## Toughness

Toughness is the ability of a metal to be deformed repeatedly without breaking, in other words a tough metal is one which cannot easily be pulled apart.

Some metals can be bent backwards and forwards or twisted or stretched many times without breaking. Imagine how useful this property is in the coupling of a railway wagon, or in the link of a chain, or the rear axle half-shaft of a heavy lorry, all of which need to yield rather than break in an emergency. Soft metals can be very tough. This is obvious when one tries to break a piece of soft copper wire by bending or twisting it. Tough metals do not machine easily because the cut metal, or chip, does not separate easily from the main body. Metals which are both strong and tough, such as nickel-chromium steels, often need special cutting tools and very powerful machine tools. But such steels are necessary for the safety and performance of many products and the engineer has to learn how to cut and join them, although it is sometimes very expensive to do so.

## Hardness

Hardness is defined as resistance to indentation. It is tested quite simply by pressing a ball-bearing or a pyramid shaped diamond indenter into the surface of the metal.

In practice, the hardness number does not need to be worked out. The indent diameter or the diagonal is measured using a microscope and the hardness number is obtained from a chart. Ordinary mild steel has a hardness number of about 200, soft brass about 100, and pure aluminium only about 20. Hardened steel has a hardness number of 700 to 800, and certain cutting tool materials 1,200 or more.

The most important point is that a metal can only be cut by a substance harder than itself. Cutting tools must therefore be made of the hardest steel or from metallic carbides (such as tungsten carbide) which are harder still. To shape these tools we must use even harder materials such as silicon carbide or aluminium oxide. These are formed as crystals in an electric furnace and are afterwards made into grinding wheels. Sometimes diamonds must be used to cut really hard metals, for there is no other way of giving them a smooth, keen, cutting edge.

It is necessary to have hard metals to resist wear. The automobile engine has many hardened parts and the ball-bearings in a bicycle, for example, have to be hard. The only way to finish steel parts is by grinding, and this is another example of how workshop methods depend on the properties of metals.

**Brittleness**

Materials which are brittle break without deforming. For instance, broken china can be stuck together again with hardly a sign of the fracture.

Brittleness is very important in engineering because brittle materials do not yield—they break without warning. On the other hand, brittle materials are usually stiff and suitable for structures which must be

*Apparatus for testing the hardness of a metal. A shaped 'indenter' is pushed into a specimen of the metal by a force recorded on the dial. Afterwards the diameter of the indent is measured.*

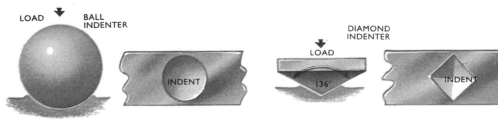

*The hardness number is defined as the ratio LOAD : SURFACE AREA OF INDENT. The load (W) is measured in kilograms and the area is measured in square centimetres. In practice the diameter (d) of the indent is measured and the hardness number is found from a chart.*

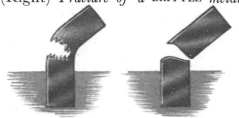

(Left) *Fracture of a* DUCTILE *metal.*
(Right) *Fracture of a* BRITTLE *metal.*

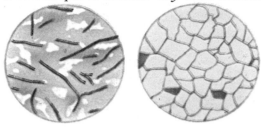

(Left) *The structure of grey cast iron. Dark lines are plates of graphite (carbon) which make cast iron far more* BRITTLE *than steel.*
(Right) *The structure of steel as seen through a microscope. It contains very little carbon.*

very rigid. Metals which are cast (i.e. made by pouring liquid metal into a mould) are often brittle. This is due to the formation of a particular kind of crystal structure from the liquid metal as it cools. Cast iron is probably the most common brittle metal. It is cheap to make and can be cast into complicated shapes including thin sections. Because of its strength and rigidity it is widely used for machine tool beds which must remain very accurate throughout their life. Even so, it can easily be broken because it is brittle and special care must be taken in clamping and handling castings. Brittle metals used in castings cannot be bent or deformed in any way, so all those metalworking operations which involve deformation are useless here. Only machining is possible. Cast iron can be treated to remove brittleness but is still not as ductile as other materials. Many metals are made hard and brittle by heat treatment and then only grinding is possible. Brittle metals will often fracture due to a blow or fall and are prone to the formation of cracks.

These examples show how the properties of metals are connected with the way they are made and the workshop processes which can be performed on them. Black steel bar and plate is hot rolled and is usually a soft form of the metal. Bright metal stock has been cold rolled or drawn. It is clean and accurate but may not be easy to deform. Castings, whether rough surfaced from sand moulds or smooth from metal moulds, are nearly always unsuitable for deforming processes. In addition, each metal has characteristic properties of its own. Copper is always soft, tough, and ductile, but its alloy—brass (copper and zinc)—can be either ductile or brittle, and another alloy—bronze (copper and tin)—can be as tough and springy as steel. Each metal has to be chosen to be just right for its job. Manufacturers use specifications which state quite clearly the composition and properties of the metal. To be successful in the workshop the engineer must know these properties and be able to deal with each metal in the best way.

# CHAPTER ELEVEN

# Fatigue in Metals

AFTER jet airliners were first put into service there occurred certain accidents involving heavy loss of life. All of the aircraft involved broke up in flight and recovered wreckage had the appearance of having been in an explosion. The aircraft concerned were eventually grounded while the cause of the disasters was sought.

After weeks of research and examination of wreckage, a whole fuselage was submerged in a giant tank full of water and subjected to fluctuating pressures. The idea was to simulate the stresses a pressurized cabin would experience in flight at high level.

After some hours under these conditions the fuselage developed cracks and ultimately failed. After modifications to the fuselage the aircraft returned to service. The cause of the disasters had been traced to a well-known metallurgical and engineering phenomenon, *fatigue*.

Fatigue is defined as a reduction in the strength at which metals fail when they are subjected to fluctuating loads. It is a very common cause of failure. An axle or a bolt that has suddenly broken for no apparent reason is a common sight. Fatigue is not completely understood. It is a very complex phenomenon and is influenced by a number of factors.

*The back axle of a car has to spin as the car moves. Each time it spins, the axle undergoes a loading cycle.*

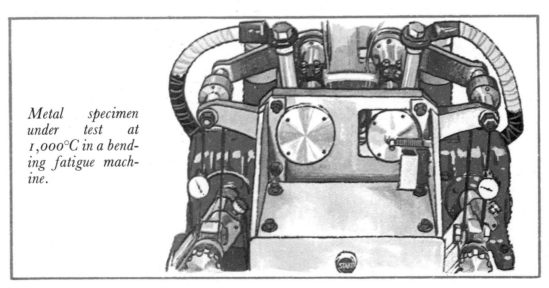

*Metal specimen under test at 1,000°C in a bending fatigue machine.*

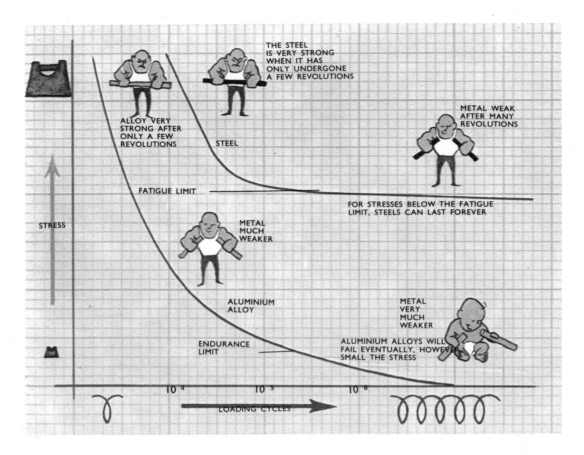

THE STEEL IS VERY STRONG WHEN IT HAS ONLY UNDERGONE A FEW REVOLUTIONS

METAL WEAK AFTER MANY REVOLUTIONS

ALLOY VERY STRONG AFTER ONLY A FEW REVOLUTIONS

STEEL

FATIGUE LIMIT

FOR STRESSES BELOW THE FATIGUE LIMIT, STEELS CAN LAST FOREVER

STRESS

METAL MUCH WEAKER

ALUMINIUM ALLOY

METAL VERY MUCH WEAKER

ENDURANCE LIMIT

ALUMINIUM ALLOYS WILL FAIL EVENTUALLY, HOWEVER SMALL THE STRESS

$10^4$     $10^5$     $10^6$

LOADING CYCLES

*Ferritic steels show a pronounced fatigue limit, a stress below which they can last for ever. Aluminium alloys will fail eventually, whatever the load.*

It bears no relationship to any other physical property usually displayed by a metal. It is difficult, therefore, to predict accurately a component's behaviour in service. Hence engineers must make metal parts strong enough to allow for fatigue when designing equipment where it may occur.

Metal fatigue depends on several factors. As an axle revolves, any particular point in the metal is being alternately stretched and compressed. The fatigue also depends on the size of the load and the number of times the rod has revolved. The temperature of the axle, the environment, whether the metal has been cast or forged and the surface finish of the rod, all play a part.

It is very difficult to forecast the fatigue properties of a metal. The best that can be done is to imitate the conditions of service as nearly as possible in a suitable *fatigue testing machine*. One type of machine uses a standard specimen. The load, temperature, environment and any other influential factors are varied as required. The machine is started and the number of times the rod revolves before the specimen fractures is noted. Alternatively, a maximum number of rotations may be chosen and the test stopped when this is exceeded.

Graphs can be drawn from the results of these tests. The curves obtained show that steels show a pronounced *fatigue limit*, i.e. below a certain stress they can last almost for ever. *Aluminium alloys*, on the other hand, will fail eventually whatever the load. For such alloys an *endurance limit* is usually specified. This is the maximum stress under which the specimen can survive a given number of rotations – say 10 million.

A cross-section of some metal that has failed shows two distinct surfaces. One is smooth with concentric ripples starting from the edge, the other rough and granular. What has happened is that somehow a small crack has started at the edge, which, of course, is the surface of the rod. As the rod has been turned, the crack has slowly spread through the cross-section, giving rise to the ripples, each one probably representing a pause in its pro-

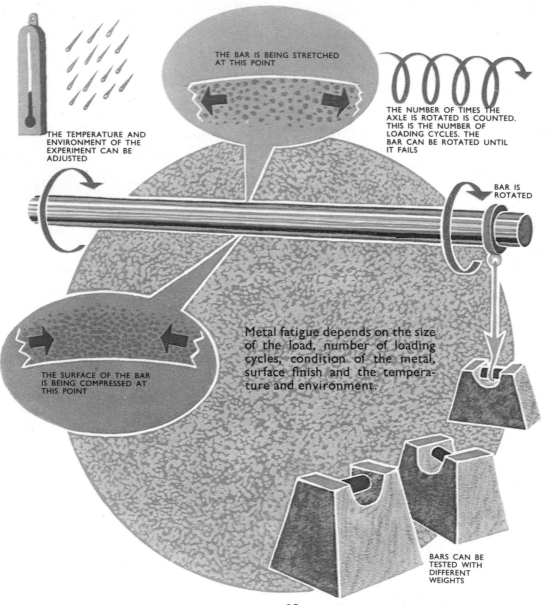

THE BAR IS BEING STRETCHED AT THIS POINT

THE TEMPERATURE AND ENVIRONMENT OF THE EXPERIMENT CAN BE ADJUSTED

THE NUMBER OF TIMES THE AXLE IS ROTATED IS COUNTED. THIS IS THE NUMBER OF LOADING CYCLES. THE BAR CAN BE ROTATED UNTIL IT FAILS

BAR IS ROTATED

THE SURFACE OF THE BAR IS BEING COMPRESSED AT THIS POINT

Metal fatigue depends on the size of the load, number of loading cycles, condition of the metal, surface finish and the temperature and environment.

BARS CAN BE TESTED WITH DIFFERENT WEIGHTS

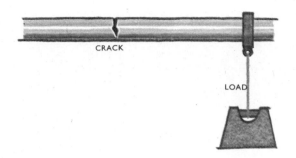

CRACK

LOAD

*The number of times the axle revolves before it cracks can be noted. Alternatively, the axle can be revolved the maximum number of times it is likely to revolve in use, to see if it is strong enough.*

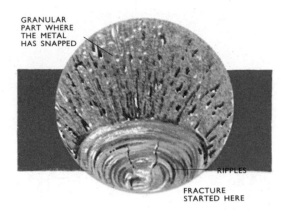

GRANULAR PART WHERE THE METAL HAS SNAPPED

RIPPLES

FRACTURE STARTED HERE

*Piece of metal which has fractured because of fatigue. The crack started at the edge and slowly spread in ripples until the metal snapped. The metal appears granular where the bar snapped.*

gress. Finally, when cracked almost halfway through, the remaining cross-section has been unable to take the load and snapped suddenly, giving the torn granular portion.

A large proportion of fatigue cracks start at the surface and it is apparent that the surface condition of the metal is of great importance.

Fatigue failures can be prevented if care is taken in the design stages. Many cracks start at a badly positioned oil-way, a machining undercut, a sharp corner or some other source of stress that could have been eliminated by a better design. One natural phenomenon that may give rise to a fatigue failure is *resonance* in the component. It may set up a stress cycle or accentuate an existing normal cycle until it is outside the safe limit. Large bodies of troops marching over bridges are sometimes required to 'break step' because the rhythmic pounding of their boots could set up resonance in

the bridge which could lead to structural damage. It is possible that the frequency of their marching may coincide with the natural frequency of the bridge and set it vibrating in sympathy until it fractures.

Fatigue in a corrosive environment is called *corrosion failure*. A corrosive liquid may cause small pits to be formed on the surface of the metal which may help to initiate cracks. But when the corrosive effect is simultaneous with fatigue stressing, the destructive effect is far greater than that caused by a notch or crack. With a microscope it is possible to see that a corrosive medium, and in fact even oxygen, causes the crack to spread much faster than it would do in a vacuum. Naturally this drastically lowers the strength at which the metal fails.

*Shot blasting. A shower of lead shot may be used to descale a metal surface before it receives a protective film of paint.*

# Corrosion and
# the Protection
# of Metals

# CHAPTER TWELVE

# Corrosion

BECAUSE iron is comparatively cheap and is also strong, it is widely used for structural purposes. It has, however, one serious drawback – when it is exposed in the (moist) air its surface rapidly becomes covered with a layer of rust, so weakening the structure. If the formation of rust is allowed to continue unchecked, the structure may eventually become so weak that it collapses.

Other metals, too, undergo *corrosion* to a greater or lesser degree. For instance, a thin black layer of sulphide forms on the surface of silver, while with aluminium, a *protective* layer of aluminium oxide is formed.

Any surface chemical action which occurs between exposed metal and its surroundings may be regarded as corrosion. The most frequent agents which bring this about are water (rain and moisture in the air) and the air itself, particularly the air in industrial areas, containing as it does hydrogen sulphide and sulphur dioxide.

Much corrosion occurs on the under side of bridges over railways. This is because the hot smoke from the locomotives contains water vapour and traces of sulphurous gases together with fine particles of abrasive solids in the soot. The underside of cars

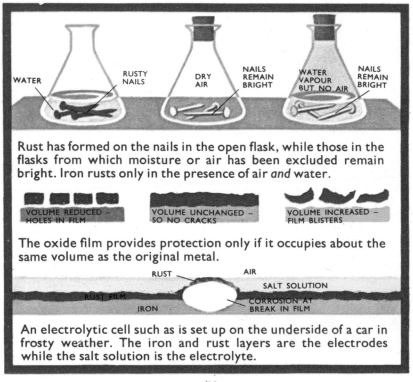

Rust has formed on the nails in the open flask, while those in the flasks from which moisture or air has been excluded remain bright. Iron rusts only in the presence of air *and* water.

VOLUME REDUCED – HOLES IN FILM

VOLUME UNCHANGED – SO NO CRACKS

VOLUME INCREASED – FILM BLISTERS

The oxide film provides protection only if it occupies about the same volume as the original metal.

RUST    AIR

SALT SOLUTION

RUST FILM

IRON    CORROSION AT BREAK IN FILM

An electrolytic cell such as is set up on the underside of a car in frosty weather. The iron and rust layers are the electrodes while the salt solution is the electrolyte.

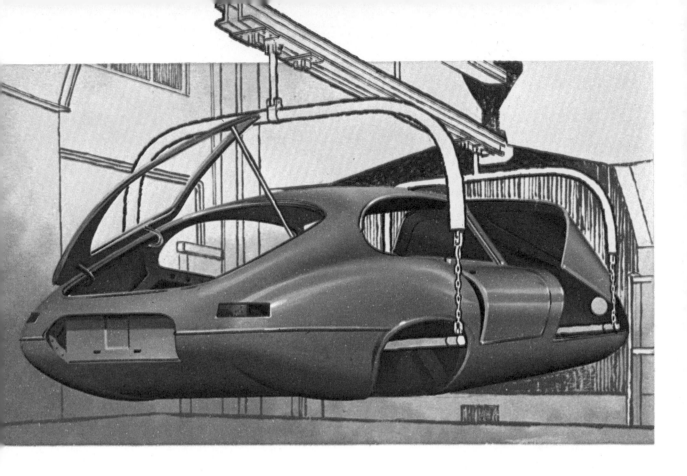

*Before a protective film of paint, plastic or another metal is applied to iron, all the rust and mill scale must be removed. There are various ways of doing this. For instance, the article may be treated chemically. This picture shows a car body about to enter a seven-stage spray plant where it will be degreased, cleaned and phosphated (i.e. a layer of iron phosphate formed on its surface).*

and other vehicles are also rather vulnerable to corrosion through water and dust from the roads being thrown up by the wheels.

The practice of scattering rock salt (sodium chloride) on icy roads in an attempt to melt the ice can lead to quite serious corrosion. It is for this reason that motorists are recommended to wash down the undersides of their vehicles after a period of frosty weather.

Many compounds attack metals and in consequence some of the material is eaten away. The chemical engineer is, therefore, frequently faced with the difficult task of choosing the most satisfactory materials (metal or non-metal) to use in the construction of chemical plant. Substances which appear to be quite harmless at room temperature may cause serious corrosion at the high temperatures and pressures which are maintained in some reaction vessels.

Much work has been done in recent years to find the causes of corrosion and the means of avoiding them. Although scientists now have a greater knowledge of the various mechanisms involved, it is such a vast subject that it is not yet fully understood. However, it is quite clear that there are a number of different ways in

71

*Although other materials are now available, red lead paint is still widely used to protect steel work against corrosion.*

which corrosion can occur and by recognising them it is often possible to eliminate the risk of corrosion while arriving at a satisfactory design.

In one important type of corrosion a solid film of oxide, sulphide or carbonate is formed on the surface of a metal – and in a few instances (e.g. aluminium) the film itself provides protection for the metal underneath. This is only possible when the layer of oxide occupies about the same volume as the metal whose place it takes.

If, instead, the film takes up less space than the original metal, the surface layer will either be porous or will crack. Corrosion will, therefore, continue because the agents of corrosion still have comparatively

easy access to the metal. A surface film which has a larger volume than the original metal affords no better protection against corrosion than does the film of smaller volume, because the scale tends to buckle or blister and fall away after a time.

In all other types of corrosion the metal surface is gradually eaten away *without* a film being formed, and because there is no film to provide protection against further attack there is no change in the rate of corrosion. The corrosion only diminishes when the material causing it becomes exhausted.

One frequent cause of this type of corrosion is the setting up of minute electrolytic cells on the surface. For this to happen it is necessary for there to be two different solids and an electrolyte in contact on the metal surface. When this condition is satisfied, corrosion continues so long as the cell produces a current. The attack is worse because the current is short circuited through the metal. It is because of the risk of establishing these cells that joints between dissimilar metals are to be avoided or if absolutely necessary are specially protected.

Electrolytic corrosion can occur between a metal and its oxide film after holes have developed in the film. This is the type of corrosion which occurs underneath cars in icy weather. Sand and grit scratch holes in the oxide scale and the salt solution provides the electrolyte. Electrolytic corrosion seems to be most severe on iron where the flow of electrons which constitute the current enters the metal.

The composition of some metals, in particular iron, tends to vary slightly over the surface. This sort of variation can also give rise to electrolytic corrosion when the surface becomes moist. Although engineers favour alloys because, in general, they are mechanically stronger than the pure metal, there is a definite risk of corrosion between the two or more constituent elements.

There are far too many other means by which corrosion can occur (e.g. in parts which are subject to varying stresses) to describe them all. The problem is particularly great in chemical plant because of the nature of materials which are being handled. But in mechanical and civil engineering, too, ways have to be found to combat corrosion.

For any set of circumstances there are two ways of approaching the problem of corrosion. It may be avoided altogether by ingenious design or by using unreactive materials. Suitable substances are not always easy to find since they have to fulfil other requirements with regard to strength, perhaps at elevated temperatures. Furthermore, they are probably much more expensive than the more conventional materials of construction such as iron and mild steel.

Nevertheless, expensive materials are often used in chemical plant. In these circumstances the use of such materials may be justified over a period of years because shut-downs for maintenance are less frequent and the product is of a higher quality. Over the years a number of special alloys have been developed for use in chemical plant fabrication.

The alternative approach is to use materials which are otherwise satisfactory and in some way to protect the exposed surface from corrosion. There are several different ways of protecting surfaces – they may be specially treated chemically with various *inhibitors* or by the application of a stable material (e.g. paint, unreactive metal or plastic).

Painting exposed steelwork has long been recognised as a means of reducing corrosion, but in order that this may be as effective as possible the metal surface must be clean, dry and slightly rough. In this context 'clean' means not only free of grease and dirt but also free of rust. Whereas on a small scale this can be achieved by scouring with a wire brush, the normal methods used on large areas are pickling in acid or by sand or shot blasting.

Once the metal surface is clean, it can be painted. The function of the first coat (the primer) is to stifle corrosion by ensuring that moisture cannot reach the metal. It must also provide a good link between the metal surface and the second coat of paint. While the second coat serves to protect the primer, the top coat must withstand the effects of the weather. The top coat may also be decorative.

In the past, red lead paint was regarded as the standard protection against rust, but this has now been superseded by other preparations which are less costly both in materials and time of application. Aluminium paint is now used extensively and recently developed coatings include the *epoxy* type of resin.

There are several ways of applying protective layers of other metals as a means of combating corrosion. Electroplating with nickel and chromium or with cadmium affords good protection and also adds to the appearance of the article. However, this is a more expensive method.

Both tin and zinc can be applied by dipping the article into the molten metal. Articles which have been dipped in hot zinc are said to be *galvanized*. This method is not particularly satisfactory since the edges, which are most vulnerable, have the thinnest coat. Furthermore, there is an upper limit as to the size of article which can be dipped.

*Sherardizing* is another (and in many ways better) method of applying the zinc coating. The articles to be coated are sealed in a container with the appropriate quantity of zinc dust. The sealed container is then placed in a furnace and the zinc is deposited uniformly over the *clean* surfaces by distillation. By this method an alloy is formed between the zinc and the surface layers of the article.

Another new technique is to direct a spray of the protective material in the form of a fine powder at the surface. Shortly before the powder reaches the surface it becomes molten as a result of passing through a flame. This technique can be used for depositing zinc or aluminium powder.

Various plastic substances can also be applied to metal surfaces to provide protection against corrosion and also to impart a more attractive finish. One method of applying the plastic surface is to use a spray of fine particles which become molten shortly before they reach the surface. Obviously much lower temperatures are needed in this operation as compared with the deposition of powdered metal by a similar technique.

CHAPTER THIRTEEN

# Chromium Plating

ITS strength and comparative cheapness make steel the most widely used metal of all. But steel has one big drawback. It rusts under the influence of the atmosphere. An ordinary steel car fender left standing in the rain soon becomes coated with a layer of scaly rust and finally crumbles away to a heap of powder if it is not given special protection. There are some steels which do not rust. These are special grade stainless steels but they are much more expensive and their large scale use is not practicable. Chromium plating is a cheaper way of solving the rust problem. It also gives an attractive shiny finish to the metal, and can be used to protect large metallic areas.

Chromium plating should really be called *nickel* chromium plating, for the real protection comes from a much thicker layer of nickel situated beneath the shiny chromium surface. Nickel is a metal which is not corroded by the

*Section through some chromium plating magnified 750 times. The chromium layer is very thin compared with the two nickel layers.*

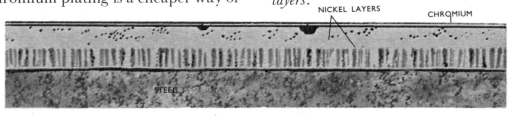

NICKEL LAYERS     CHROMIUM

STEEL

atmosphere, but it does go dull and after a time looks very drab. In the early days of plating, nickel alone was used to cover the metal surfaces. It proved to be far too soft to give the metal adequate protection, for it was too easily scratched. Deep scratches penetrated through to the underlying iron and soon gave rise to patches of rust. Chromium is a much harder metal and therefore offers much greater resistance to scratches.

As this metal stays bright, shiny and attractive it would seem to be the obvious choice for protective plating but unfortunately if a reasonable thickness of it is applied it cracks and exposes the underlying steel. In 1928, nickel chromium plating came into use, first a layer of nickel to protect the metal underneath and then a thin layer of chromium to protect the nickel from scratches and give a shiny finish.

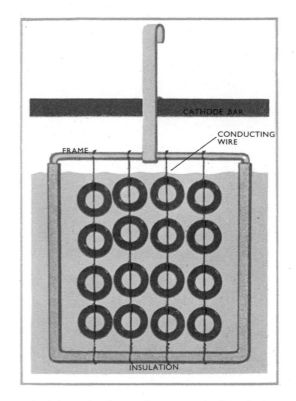

*Articles wired on a frame ready for plating.*

*Some anodes designed to obtain an even thickness of plating.*

*Electric kettles arranged on insulated jigs ready for plating.*

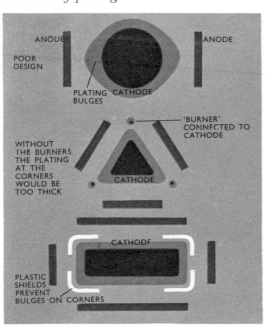

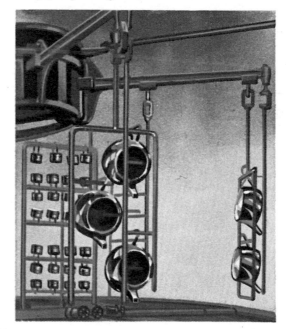

*Small articles about to be plated in a rotating barrel. The barrel will be submerged in electrolyte between rows of anodes.*

This type of plating is also used to protect brass and alloys of zinc from corrosion.

Different conditions require different plating techniques. Something which has to withstand the buffeting of wind and rain will need greater protection than an article which will always be kept dry. For this reason, objects are classified into three groups: those used for exposed outdoor service (car fenders, for example), steamy or damp indoor service (e.g. bathroom fittings) and objects such as the clip on a propelling pencil for dry indoor service. For proper protection of steel, certain minimum thickness of nickel must be applied. For severe conditions it must be 0.0012 in. thick, for moderate conditions 0.0008 in. and for mild indoor service 0.0004 in. thick. Brass and zinc alloys require less protection. The minimum chromium thickness (0.00001 in.) is the same for all cases.

Chromium plating is not a job for an amateur. It depends a great deal on specialized knowledge, as each type and shape of article needs special treatment. Whatever the nature of the article it must be thoroughly cleaned, otherwise the plating will be faulty. The metal is usually cleaned with a hot alkaline solution, rinsed and then dipped in acid before plating.

The surface to be electroplated with nickel must also be smooth with no bumps in it. Steel which has been manipulated and shaped often has a rough surface and this is difficult to get smooth. In such cases a layer of copper is plated on before the nickel because it is easy to polish the softer copper rather than the harder steel. Zinc alloy which has been die cast into various articles is also usually copper plated, in order to avoid its being attacked by the acidic nickel plating solution.

## Nickel plating

The electroplating tank is filled with a solution of a nickel salt. The article to be plated is suspended in this liquid electrolyte and connected to the negative terminal of a source of direct current. The object then becomes the *cathode*. The positive terminal is connected to an anode of nickel which also dips into the solution some small distance from the cathode. Nickel from the solution is deposited on the object and more nickel from the anode goes into solution to take its place.

The objects are seldom plated one at a time, but usually in batches. They can be either wired onto a metal frame or hung on rigid jigs or racks. The electrical current flows either through the wire or through the jig to the objects. It is preferable to use a jig because it takes less time to assemble and the object is free from wire marks. Also the objects can be more accurately positioned.

Naturally the longer the article is left to plate, the thicker the nickel deposit will grow. The thickness also depends upon the density of the current reaching the surface. When

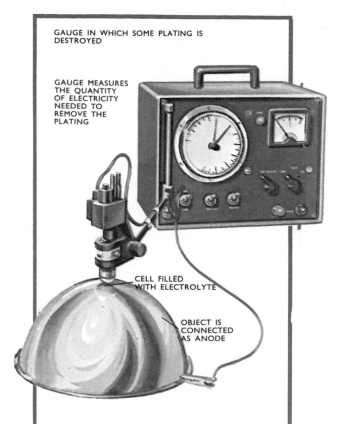

GAUGE IN WHICH SOME PLATING IS DESTROYED

GAUGE MEASURES THE QUANTITY OF ELECTRICITY NEEDED TO REMOVE THE PLATING

CELL FILLED WITH ELECTROLYTE

OBJECT IS CONNECTED AS ANODE

## Thickness checking

The efficiency of the plating depends very much on the thickness of the metal layers. The most accurate way of determining this involves taking a section of the metal and examining it under a measuring microscope. This is all right for checking occasional articles but no use for checking every one, as the plated article is destroyed. There are several methods of non-destructive checking. One is based on the e.m.f. produced when a metal junction is heated and another on the magnetic properties of the metals involved. These instruments are useful for checking each article but neither can give such accurate results as the destructive methods.

A technique which is as accurate as the microscopic method and only involves destroying the plate and not the article itself is to electrolytically dissolve a small area of the plate off the steel and check how much current is needed to do this.

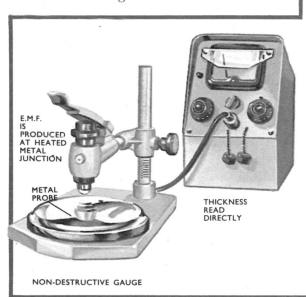

E.M.F. IS PRODUCED AT HEATED METAL JUNCTION

METAL PROBE

THICKNESS READ DIRECTLY

NON-DESTRUCTIVE GAUGE

flat anodes are used, the current density varies over the surface. The thickness of the deposit varies too unless special tricks are used to give an even coating. For example, a cylindrical object can be evenly plated by placing it inside a cylindrical anode, then the current density is the same all over the surface. If flat anodes were used the current density would be greater at the curved surface nearest to the plate.

## Chromium plating

The chromium plating is carried out in similar fashion to the nickel plating except that this time the electrolyte is a solution of chromium salts. Also the anode is not made of chromium but of lead or lead alloy, as this is much more convenient. All the chromium comes from chromium salts in solution. The lead anode is insoluble and does not contaminate the solution.

Chromium could formerly be plated only 0·00001 in. thick using the older types of electrolyte, but now great resistance to corrosion can be achieved by using one of two distinct new types of chromium plating, each obtained by using special solutions of electrolytes. They represent two different approaches to the problem of pits forming in the nickel through cracks in the chromium layer. With *crack-free* chromium, a crack-free layer of at least 0·0003 in. thickness is applied. With *micro-cracked* chromium, a thinner layer with about 700 cracks per inch of surface is used. Instead of a few large deep pits forming, a very large number of harmless small pits form under the cracks.

Chromium plating should have a long life if it is treated properly. Washing with soapy water, rinsing and drying with a leather keeps it in good condition, but abrasives tend to scratch and score it.

# CHAPTER FOURTEEN

# Propellers and Cavitation

AT the tip of a large high-speed ship's propeller blade, water is forced to move backwards at a high velocity. What effect has this on the water?

One important and inevitable effect is that the pressure in the water drops. The higher the water's velocity, the lower the pressure becomes. This is as predicted by *Bernouilli's Equation*, the basic equation of fluid dynamics. When the pressure drops, the boiling point of the water drops. With a reduced pressure pushing them back into the body of the liquid, more and more water molecules are able to

escape into the vapour state. A vapour bubble starts to form in the liquid, and quickly grows as more vapour molecules escape into it. This effect is known as *cavitation*.

So, at high propeller speeds, the water starts to boil around the leading edge of the propeller. Bubbles of vapour form in the water. Some of these *implode* near the surface of the propeller blade with sufficient force to blast off small pieces of metal, and eventually the propeller becomes eroded. This became so serious in one large transatlantic liner that the propellers had to be replaced after her

78

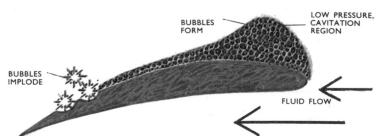

*Above: a section across an ordinary ship's propeller, with its almost-aerofoil cross-section.      Below: the sharply-pointed, propeller designed for full cavitation.*

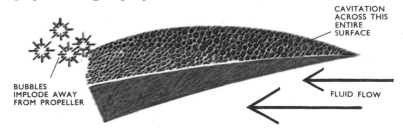

maiden voyage.

With better-designed propellers, the problem is not so acute, and even high speed vessels can be operated with a small amount of cavitation biting away at the edges of the blades. But cavitation, a form of turbulence, leads to an extra drag on the propeller blades, and causes a drop in the overall efficiency of the propulsion system.

There are no half-measures with cavitation. Propellers can be operated with none at all (or a very small amount), or a very large amount – *full cavitation* or *super-cavitation*. No propeller would last long if it were operated with a middling amount of cavitation and it would be very inefficient, so this region of operation is avoided. The jump to full cavitation is made possible by specially-designed propellers, with the flat aerofoil cross-sections reminiscent of supersonic aircraft and very sharp leading edges to bite into the water. The sharp edges are essential to reduce the cross-sectional area affected by cavitation, and hence reduce the extra drag caused by this effect. The pressures are so low under full cavitation that the bubbles implode at some distance from the surface of the blades, where they can do no damage. These high-speed propellers are used for hydrofoil craft, which cruise at around 60 knots.

Submarines are also capable of travelling at high, undisclosed speeds, but they normally travel underwater.

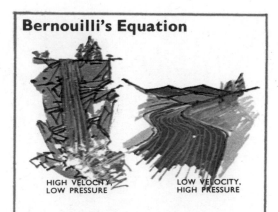

## Bernouilli's Equation

HIGH VELOCITY, LOW PRESSURE     LOW VELOCITY, HIGH PRESSURE

The main conclusion drawn from Bernouilli's equation is that the pressure in a fluid drops when its velocity increases. This turns out to be another statement of the Law of Conservation of Energy. The pressure in the fluid is unlikely to remain the same – it can either increase or decrease when the fluid velocity increases. At first sight, an increase looks more likely, but it would violate the Law of Conservation of Energy. An increase in pressure would lead to an increase in velocity, a further increase in pressure and the process would rapidly get out of hand.

Here there is little danger of cavitation. The pressure in the water increases with depth. Underwater, the pressure includes the weight of the water above, as well as atmospheric pressure. Although the pressure is lowered in the vicinity of the submarine propellers, it can never drop low enough for the water to boil and cavitation to set in.

# The Working
## of Metals

# CHAPTER FIFTEEN

# Rolling Metals into Shape

OIL cans, 'tins' for food, cor-
rugated iron, girders, railway
lines, automobile bodies – these are
just a few of the numerous everyday
items which begin by being shaped out
of metal by rolling. The process is
not unlike squeezing clothes through
the rollers of the wringer of a wash-
ing-machine. With the clothes the
idea is to wring out the water, while
in the case of metals the idea is to
squeeze them down to a thinner shape.

Basically this is what happens. The
cast ingot, while it is still hot and
pliable, is reduced in thickness by a
slabbing mill to make a slab or by a
cogging mill to make a bloom. A slab

is a piece of metal rectangular in
section while a bloom is square.

After re-heating to 1300°C., the
slabs are passed on through several
pairs of rollers, becoming thinner
and longer until finally they are
reduced to thin sheets, plates or
strips.

The blooms are similarly treated,
but in this case the aim is not to
produce a flat sheet but to obtain a
bar of a certain cross-section (i.e.
the shape when looking at one end of
the bar). This is the case, for example, with rods, bars, railway lines
and H-shaped girders. Again the process starts with rollers squeezing the

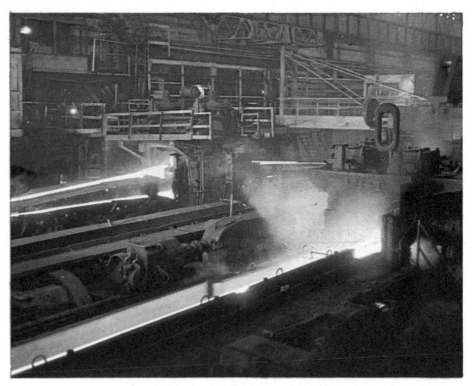

*Hot rolling of girders from blooms at a mill in Indiana, U.S.A.*

*Cutting the metal strip to its final length, using the 'Flying Shears' machine.*

bloom only a little. As it moves on the bloom passes through specially shaped rollers which bring its shape to that which is required.

In a similar process, known as cold rolling, the metal passes through rollers in a similar way but the metal is not heated. Since the metal is not so pliable, greater pressure is required but a smoother and more accurately finished cross-section is obtained. For rather complex reasons the hard-ness of the metal is also increased.

Rolling is only one of several methods of shaping metals from the ingot stage. Others are forging (hammering into shape), extrusion (pushing the metal out through a hole of a certain size) and pressing (shaping it through great pressure). Finally the metal usually has to be further worked and cut into shape in the engineering workshop.

# CHAPTER SIXTEEN

# Forging Metals

THE forging of metals is an old-established art – practised over the centuries ever since man first worked metals into tools. The basic process – heating the metal until it becomes relatively soft and then forcing it into shape with a hammer or die – is the same as has always been used by the village blacksmith. In fact,

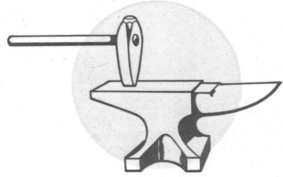

*hand forging* as carried out in the smithy is still used in different sorts of engineering work, although enormous machines have been developed for forging large metal components. In these machines, steam or hydraulic pressure systems are used to forge the work-piece.

In forging, the metal is deformed at a temperature higher than the re-crystalization temperature and an important consequence of this is that no strain hardening (increase in resistance to deformation) results in the metal. Any non-metallic impurity in the metal is spread out to produce a fibre-like structure. The work-piece then develops a great toughness and ductability (the ability to be 'drawn out') in the direction of the 'fibre-lines'.

There are a number of different categories of forging. *Hand forging* has given way, for larger components, at

*Tools used in forging.* (top) *Traditional blacksmith's anvil.* (left) *A power hammer used in the rough forging of heavy components.*

any rate, to *hammer forging*. The anvil holds the lower die, in which the metal is forged to the required shape. This might be flat, V-shaped or round. The molten work-piece is placed on the anvil and the upper die placed on the work-piece where a series of blows is delivered by a heavy steam hammer. There is a limit to the pressure that can be applied by hammer, and the largest forgings are made using hydraulic presses.

Enormous pressures are developed in these but the work-piece undergoes a squeezing action rather than the impulsive 'hammer-blow' action of the hammer. Hydraulic forging machines are the only ones capable of being used in the manufacture of the heaviest metal components. Forces of up to 50,000 tons may be developed in these. In some hydraulic equipment, in addition to the vertical ram, horizontal rams can be deployed to produce simultaneous pressings in several directions at once.

*A large hydraulic machine that shapes heavy components, using a succession of high pressure 'squeezes'.*

Another important class of forging work is drop-forging. The lower die forms an integral part of the forging machine. The impact blow is delivered by a weight-ram that holds the upper die. There are two categories of drop

*This hub, formed from a solid cylindrical steel billet, is a typical high-energy forged product. Note in the cross-sectional view, the grain pattern produced in the metal.*

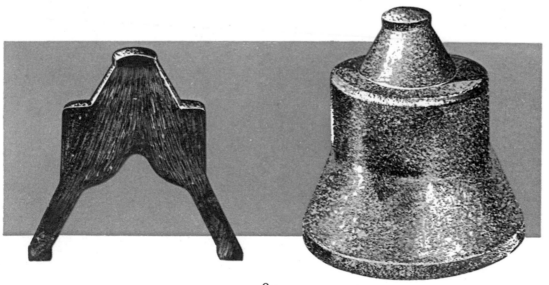

forging machine. In the *board drop-hammer* type the weight is attached to wooden boards which are raised between rollers. The weight is lifted and held up by friction in the rollers and then allowed to drop and accelerate under gravity to deliver the impact blow. In the steam-hammer, the ram is actuated by means of a steam cylinder and falls under the combined influence of the steam pressure and gravity. Very high forging forces (up to 50,000 lb. wt.) can be developed in these machines.

Drop forging is particularly useful when dealing with metals that require rapid treatment after heating. Some types of alloy can be heated through a small temperature range only, without losing some of their more desirable properties. Rapid treatment in the drop-forging machine enables the hot metal to be transferred directly from the furnace and immediately receive the forging treatment. Another advantage of the drop-forging method is that the work-piece needs very little 'cleaning up' to achieve its final form.

## High Energy Forging

One of the most spectacular developments in recent years has been the introduction of *impact forging*, sometimes known as *high energy rate forging*. To obtain the greatest efficiency in the forging process the work-piece must be subjected to rapidly delivered impact blows. The maximum energy must be delivered to the work-piece in the shortest possible time. In the conventional steam hammer and drop-forging methods considerable amounts of energy are delivered to the work-piece in a short time, but in impact forging this is improved upon.

The energy delivered by a hammer head depends on the mass of the head and on the velocity which it attains prior to impact. But the work-piece can be made to travel towards the hammer and the hammer travel towards the work-piece at the same time, so that the *effective* (relative) velocity of the hammer and work-piece is increased, and the amount of energy delivered to the work-piece much increased. This is the principle of the *impacter forging* machine. In some impacter machines the work-piece is held in a stationary position and two rams are ejected so that they come together in the plane of the work-piece. In other systems, the work-piece is placed on one of the two moving platens and once again the platens are thrown together producing a large impacting force when they meet.

The platens are energized by the application of high gas pressures in

*High pressure gas fills the system and is further compressed by pistons that are forced downwards when oil is introduced.*

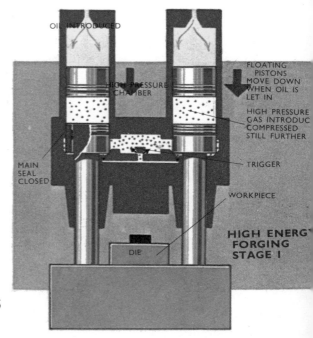

HIGH ENERGY FORGING STAGE I

86

these machines. In one type of impacter machine, the platens are connected to each other by trombone-like rods which are expanded when the platens are parted and contracted when they are brought together. A charge of gas (nitrogen) is introduced into a high pressure chamber and the two actuating cylinders at a pressure of 600 pounds per square inch (p.s.i.). This gas is further compressed by the introduction of oil into the cylinders, forcing a pair of pistons downwards under the oil pressure. The movement of the piston compresses the gas further and a gas pressure of 1,500 p.s.i. is thus developed in the high pressure chamber. A trigger valve mechanism is then operated and allows the high gas pressure under the floating piston to lift them to the previous, 'stand-by' situation, but at the same time seals off the high pressure chamber. The driving pistons are then situated between the higher pressure of the pressure chamber side, and a lower pressure on the cylinder side. This makes the pistons move with great rapidity and causes the two platens to be thrown together until they meet, at a relative velocity of 45 miles per hour.

One of the great advantages of this method is that very little energy is wasted in 'pounding' the machine frame as in forging methods. All the energy developed is delivered to the work-piece itself. This makes for a clean efficient forging operation with very little surplus metal to be removed afterwards, and largely eliminates vibration and noise. It incidentally leads to great economies in installation, because the special concrete mounting normally employed for large forging machines is not necessary.

*Left. Trigger valve is closed, so gas in pressure chamber is sealed off. But oil pressure is relieved and gas in trigger passages forces floating pistons upwards. Trigger valve automatically opens so gas can force up main piston and open up main seals. High pressure gas rushes in (right) and forces up main pistons – platens come together at high speed.*

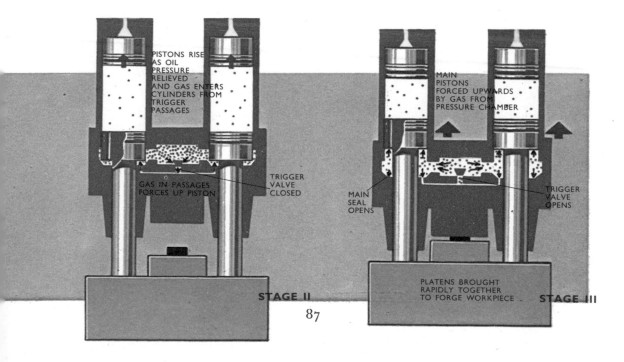

# CHAPTER SEVENTEEN

# Welding and Cutting Metals

IN bygone times a farmer with a broken plough-share would have it repaired by *forge-welding*. The local blacksmith would heat up the metal in the fire and then hammer the red-hot edges vigorously together. The edges merged into a joint almost as strong as the original metal. Forge-welding, however, is a very slow process and has now been superseded in most places by modern welding techniques.

The new methods have two great advantages: they are faster, and the equipment can be taken to the repair job. Previously, machinery parts had to be taken to the forge.

Welding is a process of joining metal by heating with or without the application of pressure. The metal is heated to its melting point and the edges fuse together. The metal cools down in one piece. Often a filler metal of similar

*Gas-welding a towel-rail. Note the welding rod, the two pipes supplying oxygen and gas to the torch, and the protective clothing of the operator.*

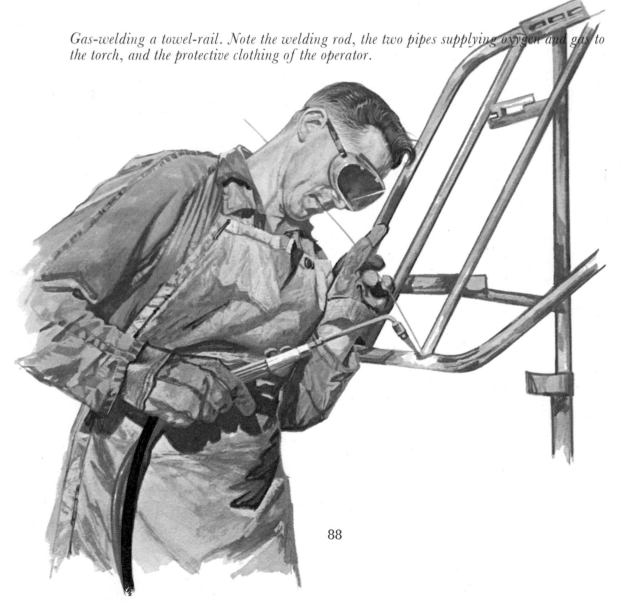

composition is used to bind the two pieces together. Heat is provided by burning a gas (hydrogen or acetylene) or by electrical means.

Metal cutting is a very similar process to welding. Heat (usually from burning gas) is used to melt through the metal and thus cut it to the required shape. The molten metal or its oxide is forced out before the two pieces can fuse together again. Both welding and cutting are used extensively in industry, for they are quick and cheap processes. Iron, steel, aluminium, nickel and copper are among the metals that can be cut or welded in this way.

## Arc Welding

This type of welding accounts for most of the welding done in the world today. An electric current is made to 'jump' a gap between an electrode and the metal to be welded. The temperature of the arc is very high (about 3600°C) and the metals melt.

Usually the electrode is of similar composition to the metal to be welded.

The heat of the arc melts the electrode and tiny droplets of molten metal are forced across the arc. This metal forms the weld. Because the droplets are forced across the arc and do not fall by gravity, welding can be done in any position. Consumable electrodes are fed gradually through the welding tool. In automatic welding, the electrode is fed in from a large coil.

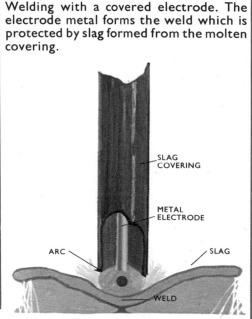

Welding with a covered electrode. The electrode metal forms the weld which is protected by slag formed from the molten covering.

SLAG COVERING

METAL ELECTRODE

ARC

SLAG

WELD

Tungsten electrode welding with a shield of inert gas. A welding rod is used and the tungsten, because of its high melting point, remains solid.

NON-CONSUMABLE TUNGSTEN ELECTRODE

INERT GAS

CONSUMABLE WELD METAL ROD

WELD — ARC

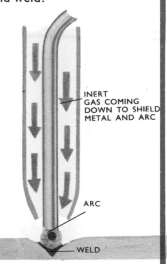

Inert gas welding. Argon or some other gas flows around the electrode and protects the arc and weld.

INERT GAS COMING DOWN TO SHIELD METAL AND ARC

ARC

WELD

Although a weld can be effected with a bare metal electrode, good quality work demands a shielded electrode and arc. Covered electrodes are most commonly used, the covering performing several functions. Various types of covering are used – containing materials such as cellulose, rutile, iron powder and lime. The covering insulates the electrode electrically and when it melts it forms a gaseous or liquid protection for the arc and the weld. Oxidation or other atmospheric contamination of the metal is then prevented and good sound welds are produced. Carbon dioxide or an inert gas such as argon or helium are also used for the same purpose, although

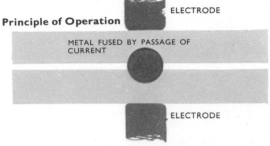

**Principle of Operation**

ELECTRODE

METAL FUSED BY PASSAGE OF CURRENT

ELECTRODE

*The principle of resistance welding. Water-cooled electrodes lead heat away from the outer surfaces and only the central part melts.*

### Types of welded joint

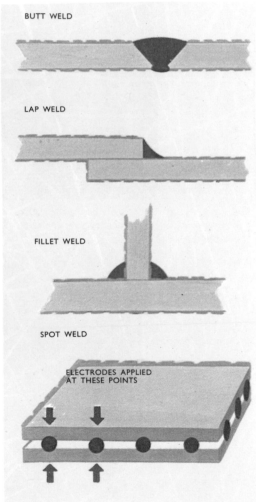

BUTT WELD

LAP WELD

FILLET WELD

SPOT WELD

ELECTRODES APPLIED AT THESE POINTS

*A resistance welding machine. The electrodes come together to make the weld when the pedal is depressed.*

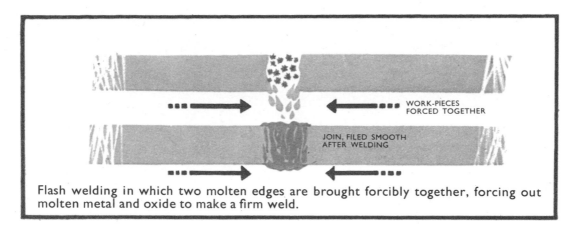

WORK-PIECES FORCED TOGETHER

JOIN, FILED SMOOTH AFTER WELDING

Flash welding in which two molten edges are brought forcibly together, forcing out molten metal and oxide to make a firm weld.

carbon dioxide can be used only with steel. Inert gas welding leaves a clean weld with no slag to be removed.

Non-consumable electrodes are also used in welding. These do not contribute to the weld and a rod of welding metal is introduced into the arc to make the weld. Only carbon and tungsten have melting points high enough to be used in this way and carbon is not commonly used for it vapourizes away gradually. Inert gas

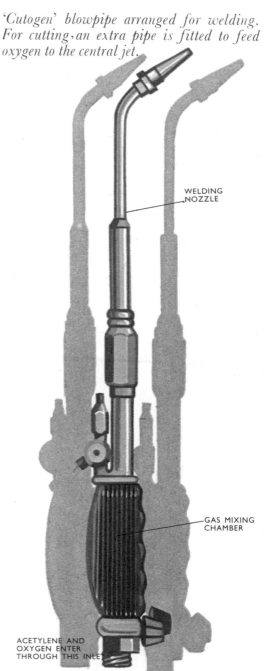

*'Cutogen' blowpipe arranged for welding. For cutting, an extra pipe is fitted to feed oxygen to the central jet.*

WELDING NOZZLE

GAS MIXING CHAMBER

ACETYLENE AND OXYGEN ENTER THROUGH THIS INLET

FLAME JETS

OXYGEN FEED

OXYGEN JET BLOWS AWAY OXIDE AND MOLTEN METAL

FLAMES

*Metal cutting with an oxygen jet. Flames from the outer jets pre-heat the metal and then oxygen from the central jet converts it to oxide which is forced away by the pressure of the jet. A clean narrow cut is then obtained.*

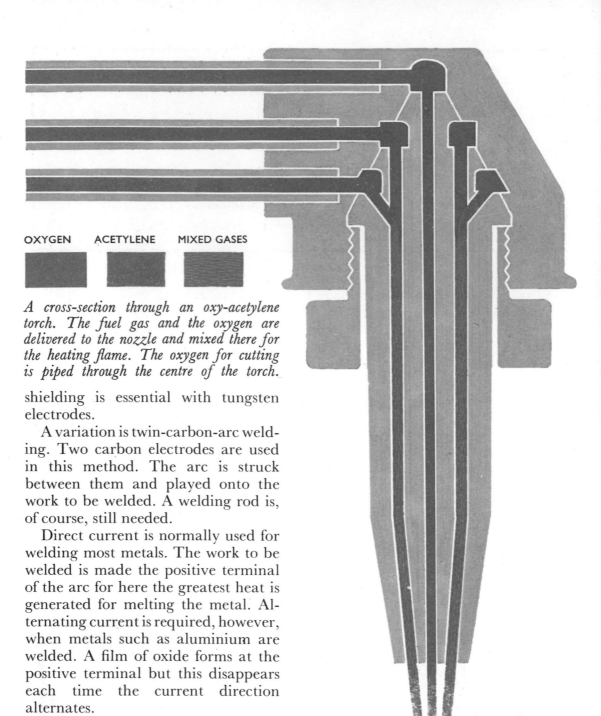

OXYGEN    ACETYLENE    MIXED GASES

*A cross-section through an oxy-acetylene torch. The fuel gas and the oxygen are delivered to the nozzle and mixed there for the heating flame. The oxygen for cutting is piped through the centre of the torch.*

shielding is essential with tungsten electrodes.

A variation is twin-carbon-arc welding. Two carbon electrodes are used in this method. The arc is struck between them and played onto the work to be welded. A welding rod is, of course, still needed.

Direct current is normally used for welding most metals. The work to be welded is made the positive terminal of the arc for here the greatest heat is generated for melting the metal. Alternating current is required, however, when metals such as aluminium are welded. A film of oxide forms at the positive terminal but this disappears each time the current direction alternates.

## Welding by Electrical Resistance

This type of welding involves the use of both heat and pressure and is especially useful for joining sheet metal. *Spot-welding* is the simplest type. The two sheets to be joined pass between two electrodes made of an alloy of copper. The electrodes come together and press against the sheets and a low-voltage, high-density current flows for a short period – up to a few seconds for thick sheets. The resistance of the metal sheets, especially at the junction between them, causes a high temperature to develop almost instantaneously. Heat is led away from the outer surfaces by the water-cooled electrodes but the central region melts. The pressure of the electrodes forces the sheets together and forms a weld. The process is repeated at intervals along the sheet edge.

Spot-welded joints do not produce a gas-tight seal and a variation known as *seam-welding* is used when gas-tight joints are required. The electrodes, instead of being two rods, are two wheels. The metal sheets move along between the wheels and a continuous weld is formed – gas-tight and water-tight.

Bolts and studs can also be welded to sheet metal by resistance heating and this does away with the need for drilling holes. The studs are placed on the sheet and then passed between two flat electrodes. The junction between sheet and stud becomes heated and the weld is formed.

*Flash welding* is often used for mass-produced objects. The two pieces to be joined are brought lightly together and the circuit is completed. Heat of resistance melts the edges and then a heavy force is applied to bring the parts tightly together and form the weld.

## Gas Welding

A mixture of acetylene and oxygen is usually used for gas welding. Mixed in equal quantities, the gases produce an average flame temperature of about $3150\,°C$ – somewhat lower than the temperature used in arc welding. Equal quantities of oxygen and acetylene give what is known as a *neutral* flame and this is used for welding most metals. Excess of oxygen gives an oxidizing flame which is useful to prevent hydrogen bubbles in some metals but must never be used with steel. Welding rods are of course necessary to provide the extra material for the weld. Various types of nozzle are used for the different welding operations.

## Gas Cutting

Metal-cutting, too, requires a special

*Using oxy-propane torches mounted on an automatic cutting machine. The torches produce very accurate spanner shapes from the metal sheet.*

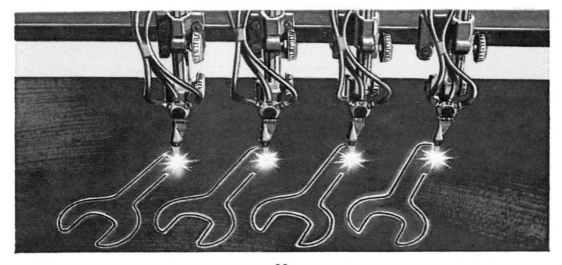

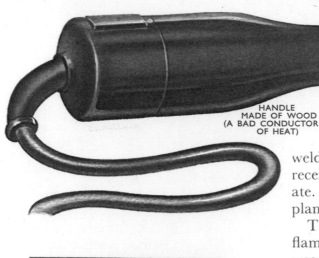

ELECTRICALLY HEATED
SOLDERING IRON

HANDLE
MADE OF WOOD
(A BAD CONDUCTOR
OF HEAT)

ALTERNATIVE BITS FOR USE
WITH ELECTRIC SOLDERING IRON

nozzle. A pre-heating flame of acetylene and oxygen issues from small peripheral jets and heats up the metal. A stream of oxygen from a central jet forms oxides which melt and are forced away from the cut. In this way the oxygen cuts through the metal.

Though acetylene is the conventional fuel gas, propane has recently gained great importance. Produced from natural gas it has the advantage of cheapness.

The cutting of metals is extremely important in industry. Shipwrights, for example, must prepare and shape heavy metal plates for the hulls of ocean-going liners. Scrap merchants need to break up large girders and castings in their yards before they can be transported to the steel works for remelting. These are only two instances amongst thousands of applications of gas cutting today.

## The Welder at Work

Before beginning to weld, the welder must clean all the metal parts. Any dirt, paint or grease may mix with the molten metal and will produce a poor weld. The edges must be prepared to receive the weld metal when appropriate. They are usually prepared by planing or flame-cutting.

The brilliance of the cutting arc or flame makes it essential that the welder wears coloured goggles to protect his eyes. Flying sparks and molten metal also make it necessary for him to wear other protective clothing such as a leather apron and gloves. Mastery of all the techniques of welding can be obtained only after a long period of training and experience.

## Soldering

Soldering is related to welding but is carried out at much lower temperatures. Metal parts are joined with an alloy (the solder) that melts below about 300°C. Common solder is an alloy of tin and lead. Soldering is normally used for joining small objects and is extensively used in joining pieces of electronic equipment.

As with welding, the surfaces must be thoroughly clean and protected from the atmosphere when heated. This is the purpose of a *flux*; it converts the *mechanically* clean surface into a *chemically* clean one by removing the oxide layer which forms on a metal exposed to the oxygen of the atmosphere, especially whilst it is being heated to soldering temperature. Removal of the oxide layer allows the solder to come into direct contact with the parent metals and 'wet' the surfaces. If wetting does not take place satisfactorily the solder will remain in beads or globules on the

POINTED
BIT

ER OVER
ING ELEMENT

metal surface and the parts will not be jointed properly.

Fluxes are classified as either *active* or *inactive*, depending upon their ability to attack the oxide layer on the metal. Active fluxes, which have acid properties, attack and dissolve the oxide layer, but after soldering is complete their residues absorb water from the atmosphere and quickly attack and corrode the parent metals. These residues are difficult to remove. Active flux may be 'neutralized' by adding an equivalent amount of alkali to form a 'neutral' salt, but this does not prevent its residue from corroding the parent metal. However, this type of residue can be removed by washing in a hot, dilute soda solution, followed by a hot water wash. Such a cleaning process cannot be performed when electrical work is involved or when contact with water would be detrimental to the joined parts. It is for this class of work that the inactive or 'safe' fluxes are used. Inactive fluxes are composed of substances which do not react appreciably with most metals at room temperature. But when raised to soldering heat they act as fluxes and protect previously cleaned surfaces.

The most commonly used active flux is zinc chloride (killed spirit), whilst the inactive fluxes are generally resin based. Both of these may be obtained in the form of solutions or paste. The inactive fluxes may also be obtained in crystal form.

The solder and the work are normally heated with a copper *soldering iron* which itself is heated electrically

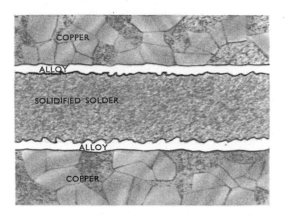

*A magnified picture of a soldered joint showing the alloy ('intermetallic compound') which tin (from the solder) forms with copper.*

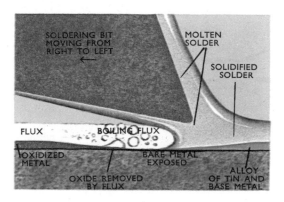

*Diagram showing how molten flux removes the oxide layer (left) and is itself displaced by molten solder (right).*

or by a gas flame.

## Solders

The composition of solders are defined by the percentage of tin, lead, antimony or silver they contain, and are selected for use depending upon the working conditions of the joint, the type of joint to be made and the metals to be joined.

*Plumber's solder* is used for joining lead pipes and cable joints. It consists of

BIT

AIR
INLET

**GAS HEATED SOLDERING IRON**

TO
GAS
SUPPLY

29% to 35% tin the remainder being lead with small antimony inclusions. This has the property of remaining pasty for a considerable time during cooling. It becomes liquid at about 255°C. and does not solidify completely until 183°C. is reached; hence it can be worked or 'wiped' to shape. *Electrician's solder* is used for making joints quickly and has the property of melting and solidifying at one temperature, approximately 183°C. It contains 59% to 65% tin, with lead as the remainder.

*Tinsman's solder* is a general purpose type of solder which melts at about 224°C. and again solidifies at about 183°C. It contains 44% to 50% tin and may have up to about 3% antimony, the remainder being lead.

*Hand soldering part of an electrical generator.*

## Metals which can be Soldered

Lead, copper, silver, sheet steel, tinplate and tin-zinc galvanized metal can, with care, be readily joined by soldering, but brass may present some difficulty depending upon its composition. Bronzes and gunmetals, too, may require special care, but aluminium and silicon-bronze, beryllium-copper, cast iron, stainless and alloy steels need special fluxes. Zinc-based die castings and aluminium are extremely difficult to solder and call for special treatment.

## The Soldering Process

The steps in making a soldered joint are:—

1. Check assembly and clean parts.

2. Tin bit and re-heat. Do not overheat.

3. Apply flux to surfaces to be soldered.

4. Remove bit from heat, place tip gently and quickly in flux to clean. Hold against solder and allow a quantity to melt onto tip of bit.

5. Tin surfaces of parts by holding face of bit against part to transmit heat to it. Run bit evenly and smoothly along surface to give a thin layer of solder.

6. Assemble parts. Reheat bit.

7. Apply small quantity of flux to joint.

8. Repeat 4 above.

9. Run the bit along the joint line allowing the solder to flow into and fill the joint. Reload bit with solder as required. Beware of overloading the bit with solder as it will only drip off and spoil the work.

10. Wash and clean part to remove surplus and solidified flux.

11. Clean the bit and allow to cool. Clean up any flux lying about on the working surface.

# CHAPTER EIGHTEEN

# Metal Cutting Tools

WORKSHOP practice might be described as the practical art of cutting up metal and fitting the pieces accurately together to form all kinds of useful products such as machinery and fittings for industrial and domestic use. Many of the things we use are made by a highly developed form of workshop practice which we call production engineering. Expensive and complicated machines are used, but if they are examined closely it is found that they use the same elementary basic principles as are used in simple workshop operations.

Although workshop practice is carried out on many different modern materials, it is still mainly concerned with the working of metals, especially steel. A lot of time, money and energy is spent in cutting up these metals, and so it is important to try to understand what happens to the metal during the cutting operation.

It is common knowledge that wood will split if a wedge is driven into the grain, and so it is very easy to cut. When a saw cuts across the grain little pieces of the wood fibres are sheared off leaving a saw cut in the wood.

Metal does not behave like this at all because it is, in most cases, strong and tough. It is much more uniformly solid throughout and not fibrous like wood.

Metal-cutting tools are not driven into the metal like a wedge but move across the surface with a kind of scraping action. The cutting point sinks into the surface by a small

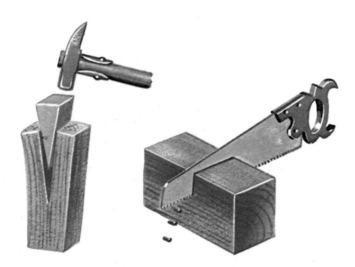

*Wood splits easily along the grain. When cut across the grain fibres are chopped by the saw.*

amount called the depth of cut. Pressure builds up at the point of the tool until it is so great that the small area of metal in contact with and ahead of the cutting edge becomes very soft and plastic. Due to the great pressure this temporarily plastic metal slides away from the cutting edge and is detached from the main body of metal in the form of a thin strip or a small curly chip. This loose material is called swarf and it is waste material. It is therefore desirable to keep the amount of machining (and the amount of swarf produced) to a minimum, and much of the skill and experience of the engineer must be directed to this end so that metal cutting can be done as economically as possible. Sometimes the chips and ribbons of swarf are collected until there is a quantity sufficient to return to the steelworks for remelting, but the best way is to produce as little swarf as possible.

If movement of the cutting edge is a straight line then the machined surface left behind by it will be straight also, and this is why metal cutting can be done accurately so that two pieces of metal, after being cut, can be fitted together very closely. But this also means that the surface must be smooth and clean as well as straight. This depends very much upon the shape of the cutting edge which always has two essential angles. One, called the *clearance* angle, ensures that the cutting edge is clear of the machined surface, otherwise the cutting edge could not sink into the metal. The part of the cutting edge along which metal slides is inclined at the angle called the *top rake* angle. This angle controls the flow of metal and, for soft metals, flow occurs most readily if the angle is as large as possible. There is a snag, however, because when the angle is large the cutting edge becomes thin and weak and easily breaks or wears. The shape of metal

If a wedge is driven into a block of steel, the material does not split like wood. The wedge is easily blunted and sticks in the metal. This is not a good way of cutting metal unless it is red hot or quite thin.

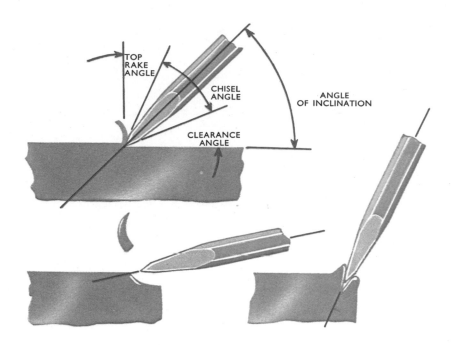

*Cutting angles are important even in a simple cutting tool such as this, otherwise a straight and uniform cut cannot be obtained.*

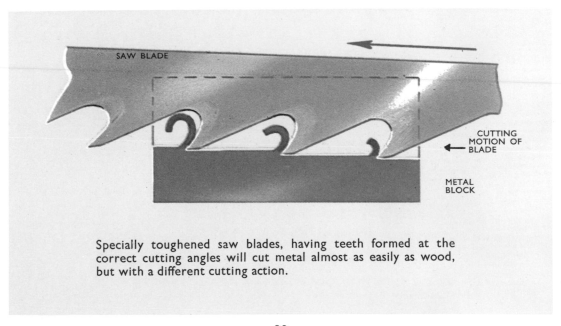

Specially toughened saw blades, having teeth formed at the correct cutting angles will cut metal almost as easily as wood, but with a different cutting action.

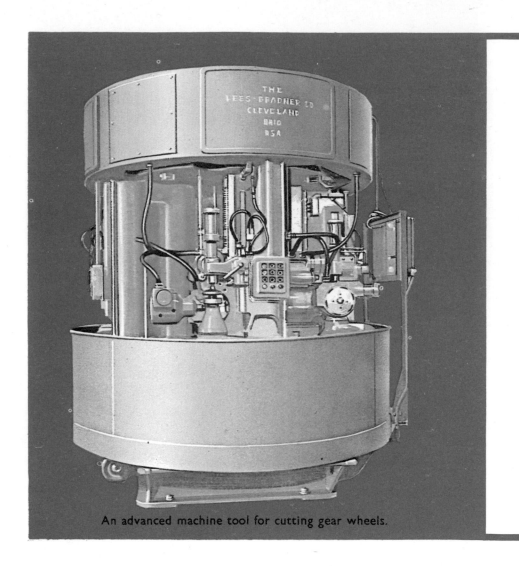

An advanced machine tool for cutting gear wheels.

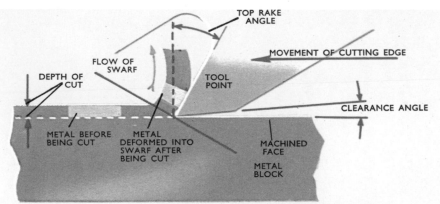

TOP RAKE ANGLE

MOVEMENT OF CUTTING EDGE

FLOW OF SWARF

DEPTH OF CUT

TOOL POINT

CLEARANCE ANGLE

METAL BEFORE BEING CUT

METAL DEFORMED INTO SWARF AFTER BEING CUT

MACHINED FACE

METAL BLOCK

The point of a cutting tool has definite cutting angles which are based upon scientific knowledge of the behaviour of metal during machining.

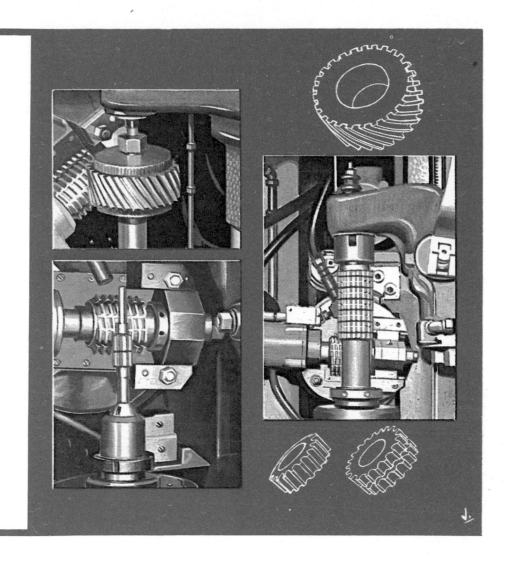

cutting tools therefore has to be carefully chosen and carefully preserved each time they are sharpened.

There are two other important things about cutting tools. Firstly the angles to which the tool is formed are different for cutting different metals. Soft aluminium requires different angles than tough steel. The engineer must therefore learn carefully the correct angles for various materials in order to do his work efficiently.

Secondly, the swarf produced has to be disposed of. The picture of the saw clearly demonstrates that the swarf can easily fill the space between the teeth. This may then either stop the tooth from cutting, or possibly break the tooth off. To avoid such accidents all cutting tools must be designed or used in such a way that the swarf is disposed of as it is produced and this is part of the skill and knowledge involved in successful workshop practice.

# CHAPTER NINETEEN

# The Workshop Lathe

ONE of the first machines you see on entering an engineering workshop is a lathe. It is a very important piece of equipment since it is used for 'turning' pieces of metal; that is, cutting them down to a cylin-

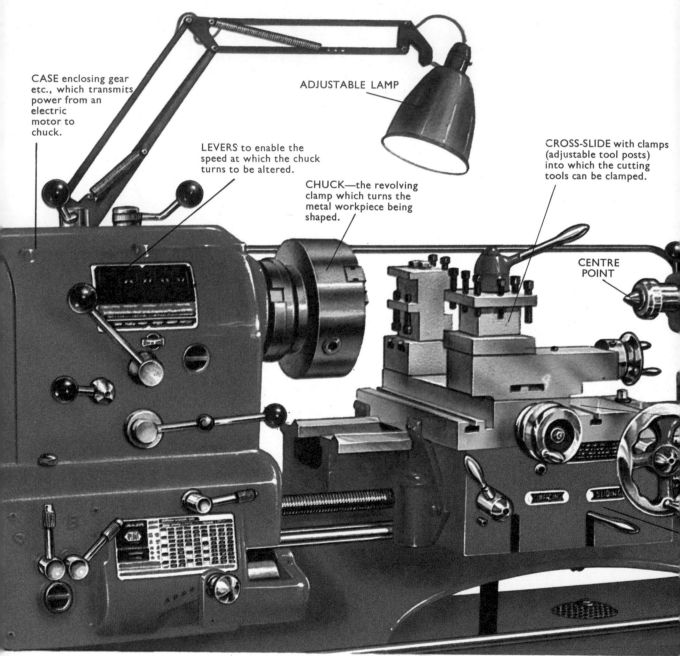

CASE enclosing gear etc., which transmits power from an electric motor to chuck.

ADJUSTABLE LAMP

LEVERS to enable the speed at which the chuck turns to be altered.

CHUCK—the revolving clamp which turns the metal workpiece being shaped.

CROSS-SLIDE with clamps (adjustable tool posts) into which the cutting tools can be clamped.

CENTRE POINT

drical shape. It has many other jobs too. It can be used for drilling holes in metal, for 'facing' a flat surface and for cutting screw threads.

The basic principle of a lathe is quite simple. The piece of metal (the workpiece) is clamped in a special vice called a *chuck*. The chuck is revolved (at a speed depending upon the type of material and its diameter), turning the workpiece with it. A sharp cutting tool, rather like a

(Drawings based on the COLCHESTER 'Student' Lathe)

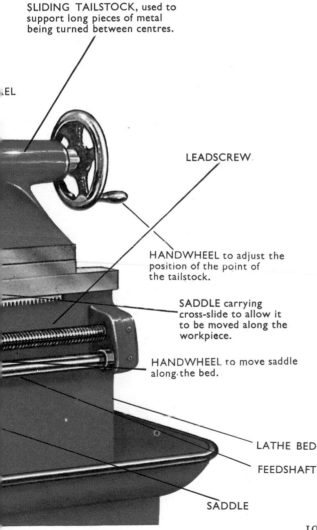

SLIDING TAILSTOCK, used to support long pieces of metal being turned between centres.

EL

LEADSCREW

HANDWHEEL to adjust the position of the point of the tailstock.

SADDLE carrying cross-slide to allow it to be moved along the workpiece.

HANDWHEEL to move saddle along the bed.

LATHE BED

FEEDSHAFT

SADDLE

chisel, is moved along the workpiece, paring the shavings from it as it revolves. If the workpiece is long it can be turned *between centres*; that is, held at one end by the chuck and supported at the other end by the point of the *tailstock centre*.

The main frame of the lathe is known as the *bed*. At the left-hand end of it is the *headstock* containing gears, which are driven by an electric motor, by means of which different speeds can be obtained. The speed change levers (which slide the gears into and out of mesh with each other) are located in the headstock casing through which runs the main spindle to the chuck. Other controls at this end of the lathe are the *clutch lever* to start and stop the spindle and levers to alter the *rate of feed*; that is, the speed at which the cutting tool moves along the workpiece.

Along the top of the bed are two pairs of slides (ways) for the tailstock and *carriage*. The inner pair of ways keeps the tailstock in line with the headstock, while the outer pair of ways guides the carriage as it is moved along the bed. The tailstock unit can be moved along the bed and clamped to accommodate different lengths of workpiece. The final adjustment is achieved by screwing the *barrel*, in which the tailstock centre is located, forwards or backwards by means of a handwheel.

The *carriage* supports the *cross slide* and *compound slide* and to the latter is attached the *tool post* in which the tool is securely held. To the front of the carriage is attached the *apron*, the whole unit being called the *saddle* which can be moved along the bed by the large handwheel at the front. When the tool has been set, the saddle can be moved along

The relationship between the speeds at which the chuck and the feedshaft or the leadscrew revolve is controlled by change gears. They are normally covered in by a casing. The relationship can be altered by fitting different sizes of gear wheels to change the ratio of the speeds.

The 'jaws' of the chuck (the revolving clamp which holds the workpiece) can be adjusted by turning a screw on the edge of the chuck. Here it is shown with a section cut away to display its workings. The jaws need to be adjustable so that they will take workpieces of different sizes and also to lock them securely in position.

Close-up of the cutting tool removing shavings from the metalwork piece as it spins in the chuck. (Inset) Detail of the cutting tool in its holder. To avoid overheating the metal during the cutting process an oily cooling liquid is poured over the affected surface to lower its temperature.

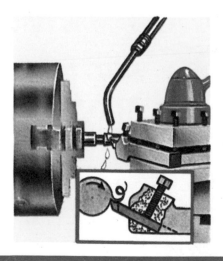

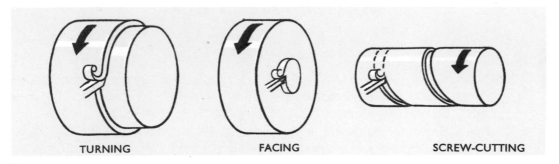

TURNING        FACING        SCREW-CUTTING

*The basic principles of three important lathe operations. (Left) Turning—spiral cuts made in the revolving workpiece by the tool moving slowly along its length produce a cylindrical shape. (Centre) Facing—the tool moves across the face (end) of the workpiece as it spins, producing a flat surface. (Right) Screw-cutting—the tool cuts spirally along the workpiece, moving along it to produce a screw thread.*

automatically, driven by a revolving horizontal shaft called a *feedshaft*.

If a screw thread is being cut the saddle is driven by the *leadscrew* instead of by the feedshaft and suitable *change gears* have to be put between the leadscrew and the work spindle so that the tool moves one *pitch* for each revolution of the workpiece, tracing out a spiral path.

The lathe can also be used to produce a flat surface. In this case the saddle remains stationary, the cutting tool being moved by the cross slide across the front surface of the workpiece as it revolves.

Because the cutting of metal produces heat, it is usual to cool the workpiece and the tool with an oil-in-water mixture. A safety device in the form of a transparent shield (not shown here) can be placed over the tool to prevent the lathe operator being injured by stray splinters of metal.

The machine illustrated and explained here is a *centre lathe*. There are many variations on it, such as the turret and capstan lathes (which speed up the process by having a number of cutting tools clamped in place which can be quickly interchanged), copy turning lathes (which can copy from a pattern almost automatically) and, of course, the wood working lathes.

# CHAPTER TWENTY

# Milling Machines

MILLING is the equivalent of wood chiselling and carving, carried out on metal. A rotating cutter with chisel-shaped blades is fed along the workpiece, cutting a groove or planing the surface according to the type of tool fitted. Milling machines are made with the spindle which carries the cutting tool horizontal or vertical, or on a head which can be turned to almost any angle. Milling machines are most frequently used for cutting slots and grooves and for making a perfectly flat surface on a piece of metal, such as a casting, the surface of which would normally be quite rough.

The workpiece is fixed to the table of the milling machine beneath the head, either in the jaws of a vice, or in the case of large or awkwardly-shaped pieces, it may be fastened with individual clamps and bolts directly to the table.

Choice of the correct kind of milling cutter for the job in hand is most important. Horizontal millers normally take cutters resembling gear-wheels, which have teeth on the outer edge and sometimes on one or both sides as well. The edge may be shaped to cut a round or V-shaped groove or even a ridge; they can be very narrow, like circular saws, for cutting narrow grooves, or very wide for planing a large surface smooth.

Vertical millers often take cutters which look and work like drills, but usually the end is not pointed and they can be used for smoothing small areas, particularly close to the ridge or wall of a part. A gear-shaped cutter on the end of a short shaft can be used to form the cross-piece of a T-shaped slot such as is used on the table of the milling machine itself for clamping. A vertical miller can also smooth large areas with what is known as a 'fly-

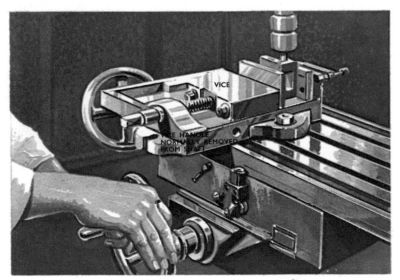

VICE

VICE HANDLE NORMALLY REMOVED FROM SHAFT

*Very often a simple vice, fixed to the worktable, is used to hold pieces to be milled. The vice handle, which fits on to the squared end of the screwed shaft, is removed for safety after it has been tightened.*

The workpiece is fixed firmly to the table of the milling machine which is then raised to take a cut of the required depth

cutter' – a tool with a single cutting edge like a lathe tool mounted on an arm so that it sweeps round in large circles, taking cuts as it goes.

The table of a milling machine is normally adjustable in three directions; vertically, from side to side, and along its length. This last adjustment is usually by hand or power, the other two by hand only. The handwheels to adjust height and sideways movement of the table are often fitted with micrometer gauges reading to one thousandth of an inch, and are used to set the depth and position of the cut. The longitudinal adjustment

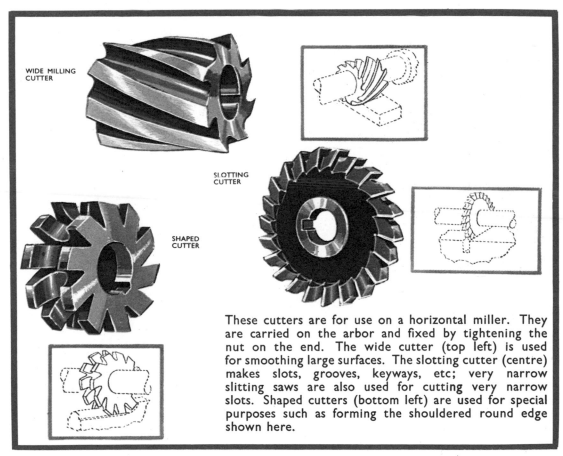

WIDE MILLING CUTTER

SLOTTING CUTTER

SHAPED CUTTER

These cutters are for use on a horizontal miller. They are carried on the arbor and fixed by tightening the nut on the end. The wide cutter (top left) is used for smoothing large surfaces. The slotting cutter (centre) makes slots, grooves, keyways, etc; very narrow slitting saws are also used for cutting very narrow slots. Shaped cutters (bottom left) are used for special purposes such as forming the shouldered round edge shown here.

can then be used to feed the work past the cutter. For delicate work it may be fed carefully by hand or the power-feed may be used. This can move very slowly indeed, and a trip can be set to stop the feed at any point.

As in lathe-work, lubrication of the cutting tool and workpiece is often necessary and milling machines are fitted with both pumps and pipes to supply a constant stream of special oil when this is required.

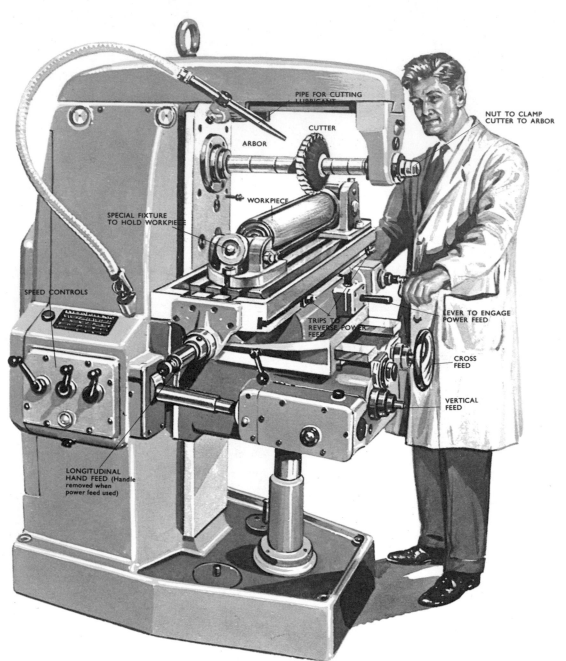

PIPE FOR CUTTING LUBRICANT

CUTTER

ARBOR

NUT TO CLAMP CUTTER TO ARBOR

WORKPIECE

SPECIAL FIXTURE TO HOLD WORKPIECE

SPEED CONTROLS

TRIPS TO REVERSE POWER FEED

LEVER TO ENGAGE POWER FEED

CROSS FEED

VERTICAL FEED

LONGITUDINAL HAND FEED (Handle removed when power feed used)

*Horizontal milling machines carry cutters on a horizontal shaft and work the metal carried on the moveable table beneath it. In this case, the workpiece is held in a special fixture.*

*This vertical miller takes a cutter in the same way as a drilling machine. The whole cutting head can be turned at an angle for milling at awkward angles. Here the work has been bolted directly onto the table of the machine.*

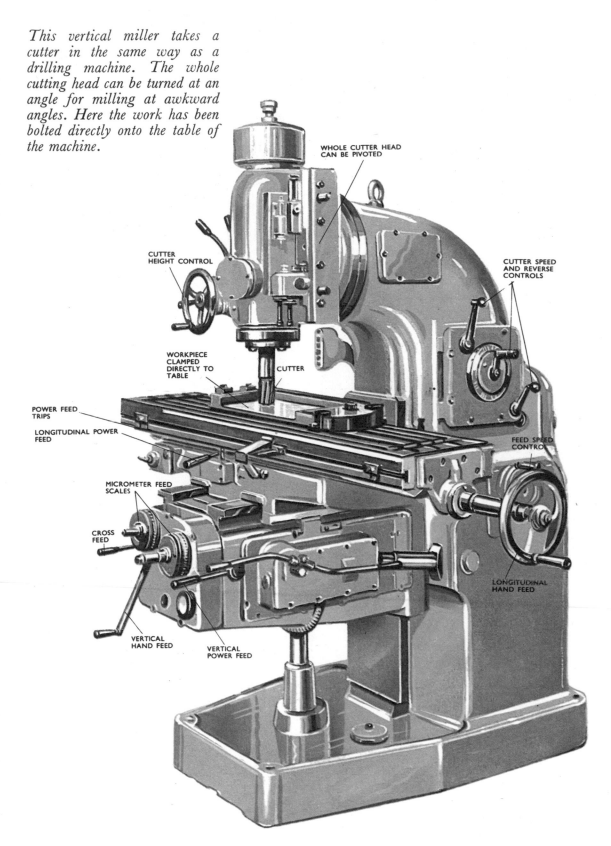

WHOLE CUTTER HEAD CAN BE PIVOTED

CUTTER SPEED AND REVERSE CONTROLS

CUTTER HEIGHT CONTROL

WORKPIECE CLAMPED DIRECTLY TO TABLE

CUTTER

POWER FEED TRIPS

LONGITUDINAL POWER FEED

FEED SPEED CONTROL

MICROMETER FEED SCALES

CROSS FEED

LONGITUDINAL HAND FEED

VERTICAL HAND FEED

VERTICAL POWER FEED

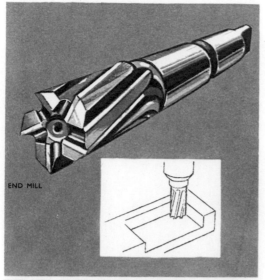

END MILL

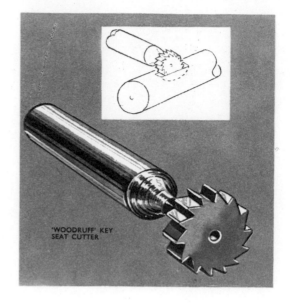

'WOODRUFF' KEY
SEAT CUTTER

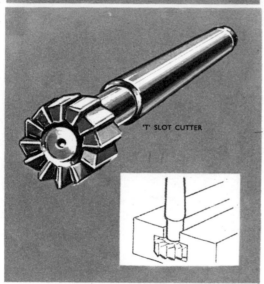

'T' SLOT CUTTER

These cutters are for use in vertical milling machines. The end cutter is used for smoothing areas which would be inaccessible to a horizontal milling cutter. The Woodruff cutter is specially made for cutting the special grooves in shafts for moonshaped Woodruff keys, the flat edge of which fits into a groove on the inside of a wheel to be fixed to the shaft. The similar 'T' slot cutters are used for cutting the inverted head of the 'T' after a plain slot has been milled with an ordinary slotting cutter.

# CHAPTER TWENTY-ONE

# Drilling and Reaming

ONE of the most common operations in any machine shop is drilling. In the home too, 'do-it-yourself' men take drilling almost for granted, but it is easily forgotten that there is a right and a wrong way to drill, as with any other machining operation.

Twist drills are nowadays almost universally used, since they are mass-produced and readily available at very low cost. The simplest form of drill, made by flattening the end of a steel bar and grinding a sharp point on it may still be used for special purposes, or when a drill has to be made up urgently.

Drills may be used in large bench-type drilling machines, in which the work is brought to the machine, or in small hand-held tools (powered by electricity, compressed air or by hand), when the drill is taken to the work. They are also very often used in lathes, where, usually, the workpiece rotates and a stationary drill is fed into it.

Drill bits are made the exact size of the hole which is to be drilled, normally from a sixteenth of an inch to one inch in diameter, although drills as small as one two hundred and fiftieth of an inch in diameter are available. Larger holes would normally be first drilled with a fairly small pilot hole and then bored out with a special tool. Holes which must be an exact size, for example for forming a bearing in an engine, are usually first drilled slightly undersize, and then *reamed* out to the exact dimensions.

Twist drills are usually made with a *cutting angle* of fifty-nine degrees, and a *clearance* angle of between five and ten degrees. These angles are suitable for general work, but drills for working one kind of metal only may be ground to different angles. For example, drills for working cast iron or brass are better with rather more pointed tips of about forty-five degrees, while hard steels are drilled more easily with less pointed drills having about seventy-five degree cutting angles.

Although in hand held tools the speed is not usually adjustable, drilling can be done more quickly and the bit will require less frequent re-sharpening if the correct speeds are used. Speeds vary, of course, with the size of the drill, and also with the metal; brass being able to stand almost twice the

*A large machine-shop drilling machine can be fitted with several drills, or reamers, which can be used in quick succession.*

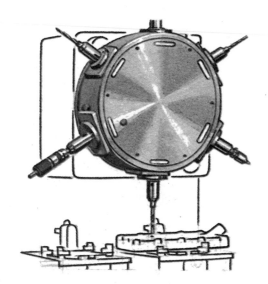

*An air-powered drill used for drilling bolt-holes in a large tank.*

speed most suitable for steel. A reasonable speed for a half inch diameter hole in steel would be about one hundred revolutions per minute (rpm). For a hole half the size, twice the speed would be necessary and vice versa (e.g. $\frac{1}{4}''$ diameter – 200 rpm, $\frac{1}{16}''$ diameter – 800 rpm, 1" diameter – 50 rpm). With small hand-held power drills these speeds cannot usually be kept to, but provided care is taken not to allow the bit to over-heat (oil can be used to cool it) and provided 'high-speed' bits are used, they can be expected to remain sharp for quite a long time.

## Reaming

When holes have to be made completely circular and to very accurate dimensions, they are usually reamed out from a slightly smaller drilled hole. The reamer often looks like a straightened out and blunted drill bit, or it may have a very slight twist on it. It does not cut metal at its end, like a drill, but all along its sides. Reamers are often screwed in by hand, fixed in a simple handle, or they may be used in a bench-drill at very low speeds. They can be only very slightly larger than the drilled hole they are to enlarge, although adjustable reamers are used which can be gradually enlarged in between successive cuts. Taper reamers are sometimes used when a tapered hole is required. The hole is drilled fractionally smaller than the smallest end of the hole required, and the reamer then fed in and turned until it has enlarged the hole as much as required.

*(top) A parallel sided reamer. (below) An ordinary twist drill.*

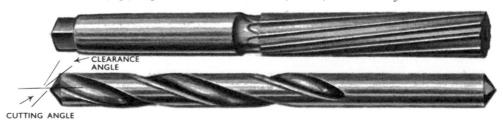

CLEARANCE ANGLE

CUTTING ANGLE

# CHAPTER TWENTY-TWO

# Screws

IT is a strange household that has no box of screws hoarded somewhere ready for joining a broken piece of woodwork or doing odd repairs around the house. Nor will this box always be filled with identical screws. Some will be black, some brassy, some silver coloured. There will be long ones, short ones, fat ones, thin ones, screws with sharp ends and others with blunt ends; in fact, a wide range of assorted screws.

This is hardly surprising, for screws feature in so many different articles for so many purposes and obviously different types of screws are needed to do different jobs. No one would expect an aircraft wing to be held in place by the same type of screw used for fixing a chair leg. In fact, one particular firm manufactures over 19,000 various forms of screw.

Whether they have rounded or flat tops, most screws have a straight groove cut into the head so that the screwdriver will slot into it. It has been realized recently that this is not the best design because the screwdriver can easily slide along the groove and plough into the surface of the article, or worse still, injure the person using it. Some more modern designs have a cross-shaped hollow in the centre of the head and require a screwdriver of the same shape. In these, as there is no path to the edge of the screw, the screwdriver cannot slip.

The materials of which the screws are made also differ. The vast majority are made of steel wire. Sometimes these are given a protective plating with substances such as nickel. Stainless steel screws are used in bathrooms and in boats above the water line. Below the water line, though, they tend to corrode, and corrosion-proof screws of silicon bronze are used instead.

Basically, screws fall into two distinct groups – *wood screws* for use with wood and *machine screws* for use with metals. The wood screws taper to a point so that they can be driven straight into the wood, making their own hole and cutting their own groove at the same time. But metal is far too tough for this and instead, blunt ended machine screws are usually used in conjunction with a nut which already has the correct sort of screw thread cut inside it.

Some screws made of hardened steel do cut their own thread into the metal. These are known as *self-tapping* screws. Some of them have pointed ends like wood screws; others are blunt ended. But the main body of the self-tapping screw is straight and does not taper as in wood screws.

There are two ways of inserting a self-tapping screw. A hole slightly smaller than the screw can be drilled right through the metal and then, when the screw is inserted, it forms its own thread around the already existing hole. Alternatively, the screw can be given a start by punching a hole in the surface and then driven in so that it cuts its thread at the same time.

All small screws are made from pieces of metal wire, chopped into suitable lengths. There is no need for the wire to be heated first (though with much larger screws, such as those used in locomotives, the metal does have to be pre-heated before it can be worked).

## Manufacture of wood screws

The pieces of machinery which make these screws are usually quite small and compact. At one end of the machine is a roll of wire assembled on a turntable which revolves and unravels the wire as it feeds into the machines. First of all the wire is cut into pieces of suitable length called *blanks*. The head of the screw is formed and cutting the thread is the final operation. Usually one machine cuts the blank and 'heads' the screw and another cuts the thread.

(Above) *A heading machine. The heading tool is about to give the blank a sharp blow, squashing the head.*
(Below) *Rolling the thread onto a machine screw.*

## Heading

Part of the machinery holds the blank in a vice-like grip. The vice widens out near one end so that it is no longer in contact with the blank protruding from it. A mechanical hammer gives this end of the blank a sharp blow, squashing it into the shape of the hollow end of the vice. If the screw has a flat head then a flat headed hammer is used. Hammers with a hollow curve are used to make round headed screws. Sometimes the head is machined smooth and afterwards a small circular saw cuts a slot in it. With the slower older types of machine it was often possible to follow the passage of a blank through the machine and see quite clearly what was happening. Although the principle is still the same, modern machinery is far too fast for this, often processing screws at the rate of 4 a second.

On another machine, mechanical 'fingers' place the blank in a revolving chuck so that a sharp tool can cut the thread. The screw revolves about its axis while the sharp tool moves horizontally across, scooping a groove out of the revolving blank. As the screw is to taper off, the tool moves in towards the point of the screw so that more metal can be removed from this part of the blank. Before packing, the screws are inspected.

## Manufacture of machine screws

Only the making of the thread differs from wood screws. As machine screws or bolts are parallel sided and do not taper off, the thread can be *rolled* on. The rolling machine has two hardened strips of metal, each covered with sloping grooves of the same type and shape. The headed blank is wedged vertically between the two. The back strip remains stationary but

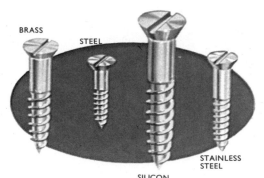

*Some wood screws.*

*Some machine screws.*

*Some self-tapping screws.*

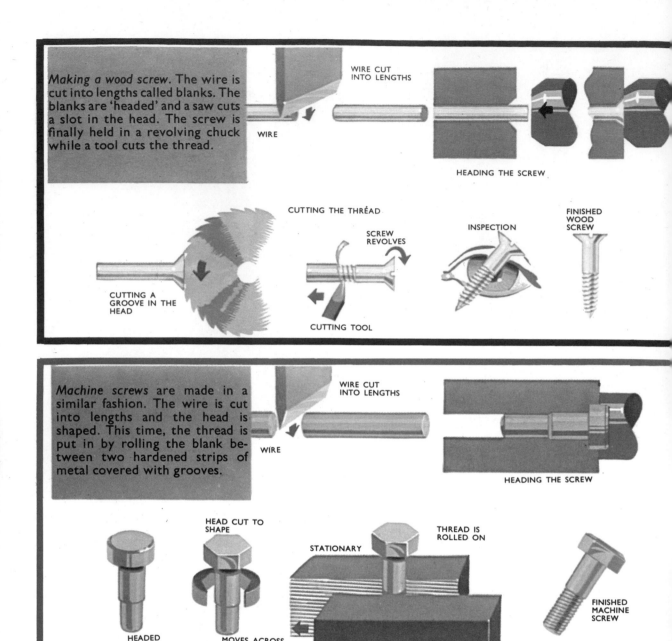

**Making a wood screw.** The wire is cut into lengths called blanks. The blanks are 'headed' and a saw cuts a slot in the head. The screw is finally held in a revolving chuck while a tool cuts the thread.

WIRE

WIRE CUT INTO LENGTHS

HEADING THE SCREW

CUTTING THE THREAD

SCREW REVOLVES

CUTTING A GROOVE IN THE HEAD

CUTTING TOOL

INSPECTION

FINISHED WOOD SCREW

**Machine screws** are made in a similar fashion. The wire is cut into lengths and the head is shaped. This time, the thread is put in by rolling the blank between two hardened strips of metal covered with grooves.

WIRE

WIRE CUT INTO LENGTHS

HEADING THE SCREW

HEAD CUT TO SHAPE

STATIONARY

THREAD IS ROLLED ON

HEADED BLANK

MOVES ACROSS ROLLING THE SCREW

FINISHED MACHINE SCREW

the front one moves across its face blocking it from view while it rolls the screw along with it until the screw finally drops out at the far end.

The nuts which go with the machine screws also have to be given a thread. They too start out as pieces of wire or metal strips which are cut into lengths and pressed into shape. The screw thread is then drilled out of the solid metal with a tool called a *tap*. The tap is made of hardened steel and has the thread running round the outside of it. The thread is not complete. There are three grooves scooped out of it to allow the metal shavings to drop clear and not clog the machinery. The nuts too are inspected before packaging.

116

# Measuring
# Metals

# CHAPTER TWENTY-THREE

# Machine-shop Gauges

IN any engineering works a large number of special gauges are used for measuring the parts being made. The most common are micrometer gauges, vernier calipers and dial gauges. These are all capable of measuring a wide range of thicknesses. Other gauges are feeler gauges, slip gauges, thread gauges and a variety of special 'go-no-go' gauges for checking particular parts. These are all fixed gauges and can measure only one dimension.

Slip gauges are by far the most accurate, being ground to an accuracy of about one millionth of an inch. They are used as the *standard* of measurement in a machine shop, and the accuracy of other instruments is checked against them.

Nothing can be made exactly the right size. A part can be made so nearly the right size that the variation could not be detected with the most precise gauge available, but it is important to know just how accurate a part is. Normally a dimension is marked on a drawing as, for example, 1 inch $\pm$ 0·005 which means that it must be between 0·995 inches and 1·005 inches. Sometimes the tolerance, as this is called, is positive or negative only instead of plus or minus ($\pm$). In this case it might be marked 1 inch $\pm \frac{0·000}{0·005}$, meaning that it may be up to 0·005 inches smaller but no bigger than one inch.

These measurements are all given in thousandths of an inch (or 'thous'), a

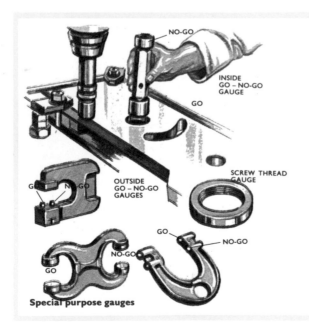

NO-GO

INSIDE GO – NO-GO GAUGE

GO

SCREW THREAD GAUGE

OUTSIDE GO – NO-GO GAUGES

GO N GO

GO

NO-GO

GO

NO-GO

**Special purpose gauges**

**Special 'Go-no-go' snap gauges**

When many parts are being made and have to be checked for accuracy, it saves a lot of time and avoids risk of error if a special gauge is made, instead of each part being measured with, say, a micrometer.

One type of gauge is the go – no-go gauge. To measure an outside diameter this would have arms like those of a vernier caliper but fixed rather than adjustable. One pair would be just wide enough to fit over the part, one pair just too narrow. Thus the part is proved to be neither too big nor too small. The actual difference in the size of the gaps between each pair of arms, depends on the *tolerance* for the part; that is, the amount by which it is allowed to vary above or below the nominal or design size.

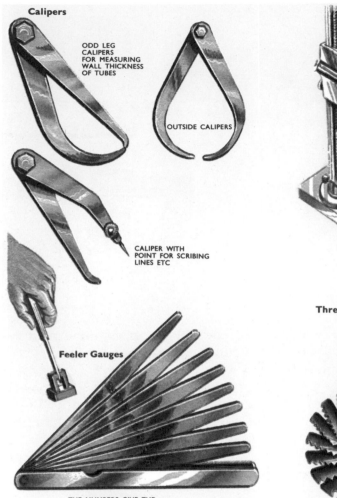

Calipers

ODD LEG
CALIPERS
FOR
MEASURING
WALL THICKNESS
OF TUBES

OUTSIDE CALIPERS

CALIPER WITH
POINT FOR SCRIBING
LINES ETC

Feeler Gauges

THE NUMBERS GIVE THE
THICKNESS OF EACH GAUGE
IN THOUSANDTHS OF AN INCH

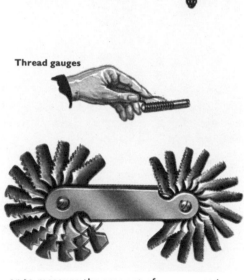

Dial or Clock gauge

Thread gauges

## Calipers

These cannot be used to measure anything
directly, but only to transfer the size of a
part to another instrument – ruler, micrometer or slip gauge, or the other way about,
to transfer a given measurement to a part to
see if it is correct or to make a mark on it.
Calipers are made in many shapes and sizes,
inside, outside, odd leg, with sharp points
for scribing lines and so on.

## Feeler Gauges

These are made for measuring small gaps,
such as between parts of machinery to allow
it to run freely. They are usually made in
thicknesses from $1\frac{1}{2}$ thou to 25 thou, and
two or more may be used together to make
up odd thicknesses.

## Dial or Clock Gauge

Dial gauges, unlike a micrometer, do not
measure actual distances but can be used to
compare two lengths and show the difference in thousandths of an inch. They can be
used with a slip gauge to measure a thickness,

or to measure the amount of movement in a
part, such as backlash on a gear-wheel.

## Thread Gauges

It is very useful to be able to recognise the
particular thread which is cut on a bolt or
nut or other part. There are many types of
thread in common use, the main ones being
British Standard Whitworth (BSW), British
Standard Fine (BSF), American Fine (AF) or
Unified Fine(UNF), Unified Coarse (UNC)
and Metric sizes. The pitch or number of
threads per inch for each type of thread
varies with the particular diameter of the
bolt. Thread gauges, looking like tiny saw
blades, fit and so identify their correct
thread. In shops where threads are being
made, more solid thread gauges are often
used to check that a thread is of the right size
and pitch. These often work on the go – no-go
principle, of one which will screw up easily,
showing that the thread is of the right pitch
and not too large and one which will just not
screw on, showing that the thread being
tested is not too small.

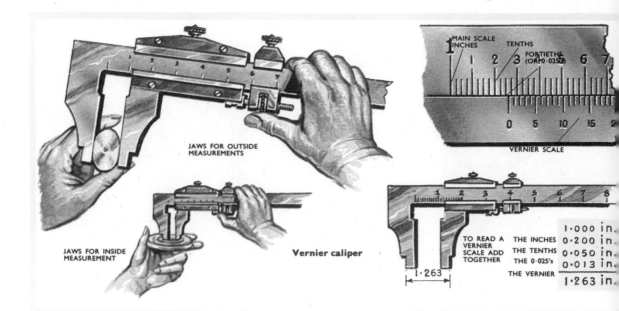

JAWS FOR OUTSIDE MEASUREMENTS

JAWS FOR INSIDE MEASUREMENT

**Vernier caliper**

MAIN SCALE INCHES · TENTHS · FORTIETHS (OR 0·025's)

VERNIER SCALE

| TO READ A VERNIER SCALE ADD TOGETHER | THE INCHES | 1·000 in. |
| | THE TENTHS | 0·200 in. |
| | THE 0·025's | 0·050 in. |
| | THE VERNIER | 0·013 in. |
| | | 1·263 in. |

1·263

common unit of size used in engineering. Micrometers measure easily to one thou, and the best vernier calipers can also be used to this accuracy. But for measuring ten-thousandths or tenths of a thou, a micrometer with a vernier scale, or a dial gauge used together with slip gauges is necessary. For even smaller tolerances, very much more complicated measuring devices would be required. The matter of accuracy is very important. It would be no good a draughtsman specifying an accuracy of $\pm$ 0·00001 inch (one hundred thousandth of an inch), if his workmen only had ordinary machine tools and micrometers. They could not

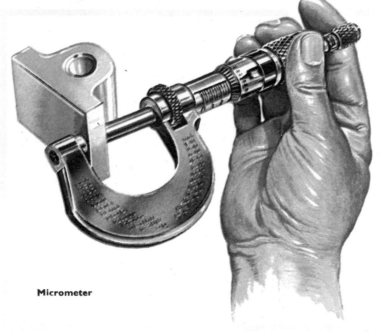

**Micrometer**

### Micrometer
This is the most familiar gauge in the machine shop. It can be used to measure to one thousandth of an inch ('one thou') or, when provided with a vernier scale, to a tenth of a thou (1/10,000 inches). The range is usually only one inch for any particular instrument, that means that they are made for measuring from 0 to 1 inch or from 1 to 2 inches and so on up to as much as 72 inches. They can be obtained in many kinds of special shape for measuring in awkward places or for measuring soft substances such as paper or cardboard and so on.

## Vernier Calipers

These can be used for measuring thicknesses and also internal sizes, such as the diameter of a hole and often, too, it can be used as a depth gauge. It is less sensitive than a micrometer but has a wider range, often 0–6 inches. To use the vernier caliper, close (or open) the jaws so that they very lightly clamp the part to be measured.

The caliper may be read in position, or more easily locked and slid off to be read.

Inches, tenths and fortieths or (0·025's) are read on the main scale. Then the vernier scale is used to find the number of thousandths, which is given by the number of the line on the vernier scale which is exactly opposite a line on the main scale.

SLIP GAUGE USED FOR SETTING SPECIAL TEST MICROMETER

make anything that accurate, nor could they measure what they had made sufficiently accurately to tell whether it met the limits or not.

Similarly there would be no point in measuring, say, a 100-yard race track to anything more precise than the nearest inch, because the watches used to time the runners could not detect the difference in time between a race over 99 yards 2 feet $11\frac{1}{2}$ inches and one an inch longer. In fact it would take about $\frac{1}{360}$ seconds longer for a runner travelling at 20 m.p.h. whereas few stop-watches measure anything less than a hundredth of a second.

## Slip Gauges or Gauge Blocks

The most basic gauge in any machine shop and the most accurate, the slip gauges are merely little blocks of very hard metal ground completely flat and to very precise dimensions – often to within a millionth of an inch. Each gauge is marked with its thickness and two or more can be used together to make up odd sizes. So smooth are their surfaces that they will stick or cling together because there is no room for air between the two blocks and so the air pressure on their other surfaces holds them together. Slip gauges may be used on a surface plate with a dial gauge to compare a thickness with the gauge, or directly to check the gap between two parts (particularly to check the accuracy of a special go – no-go gauge) or in a special adjustable frame to make a snap gauge.

**Slip gauges**

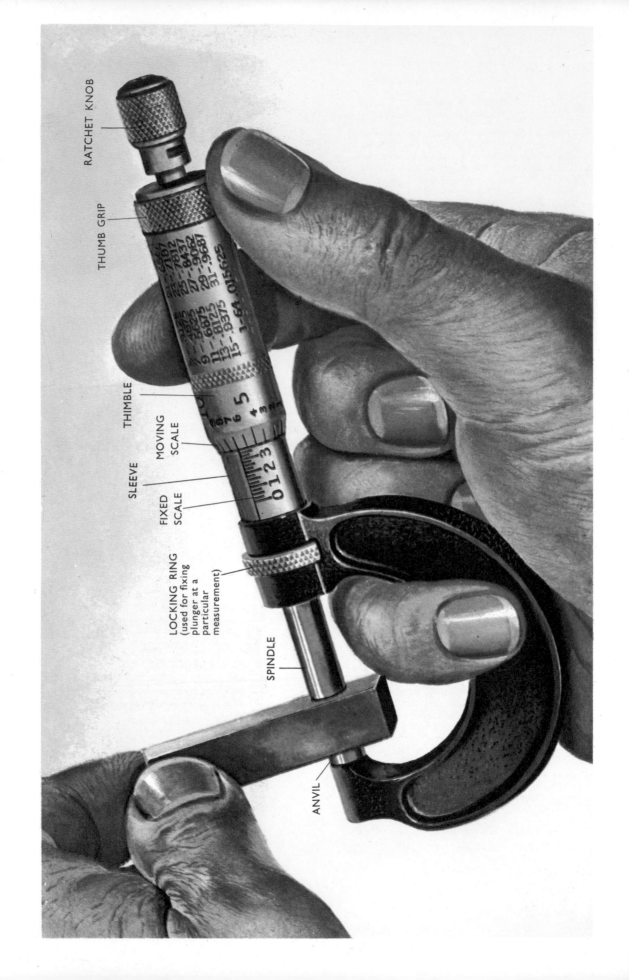

# CHAPTER TWENTY-FOUR

# Using a Micrometer

THIS instrument is commonly used for measuring lengths between one thousandth of an inch and a few inches. With care it will give an accuracy of better than 1 part in a thousand. The type of micrometer (or, to give its full name, 'micrometer screw gauge') illustrated here is designed for the precise measurement of small thicknesses in engineering.

The object being measured is placed in the 'mouth' of the micrometer and the thimble is rotated to screw out the spindle. When the object is firmly held between the spindle and the anvil, its thickness is read off directly from a scale cut into the sleeve – the inner part of the stem which does not rotate. Another set of numbers engraved on the bevelled edge of the thimble and used in conjunction with the fixed scale gives readings to the nearest thousandth of an inch.

The principle of the micrometer is simply that when any screw is turned through one complete rotation, it advances by an amount equal to its *pitch*, i.e. the distance between successive threads.

In the instrument illustrated the screw thread (which is cut spirally around the concealed end of the spindle) has a pitch of $\frac{1}{40}$ (one-fortieth) of an inch. The outer moving part of the thimble is attached to the spindle and turns with it. Because the thimble is rather wide, any point on it moves through a distance of roughly $1\frac{1}{4}$ inches during a complete revolution. The spindle advances by only one-fortieth of an inch in a complete revolution, so the movement of the thimble is 50 times as great as the movement of the spindle ($1\frac{1}{4}$ is equal to fifty-fortieths). The scales can be read like a ruler to the nearest twentieth of an inch, so a spindle movement of only one thousandth of an inch can, after it has been magnified 50 times by the screw, result in a readable movement of $\frac{1}{20}$ inch on the moving scale.

The accuracy of the instrument depends upon the precision with which its screw thread has been cut and cared for. The ratchet knob is a device which protects the thread from damage due to screwing the spindle too tightly against the anvil or the object being measured. As soon as the spindle meets the object or comes into contact with anything solid the ratchet knob slips round without turning the stem.

# Steps in Using a Micrometer

**1.**

The micrometer is held in the right hand so that the scale is clearly visible to the operator.

The first step before using a micrometer is to check the zero reading. To do this it is necessary to close the mouth of the instrument by turning the ratchet knob only. When the ratchet knob begins to slip round both the fixed and moving scales should read 'o'. Whatever reading is obtained with the mouth of the instrument closed must be *subtracted* from all subsequent readings.

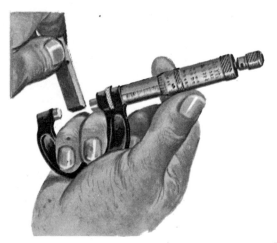

**2.**

The next step is to rotate the thimble anti-clockwise between the thumb and forefinger, holding the instrument as shown, until the mouth of the instrument is wide enough to fit over the specimen. It will probably be found more comfortable to use the roughened ring near the moving scale instead of the main thumb grip at the end of the thimble. With the specimen in place the thimble is turned gently clockwise to close the mouth of the micrometer.

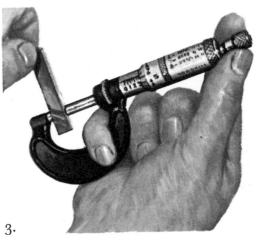

**3.**

Just before the specimen becomes clamped between the anvil and the spindle the thumb and forefinger are transferred to the ratchet knob and the final rotation done from there. This ensures firstly that the important screw thread is not put under any strain and secondly that the specimen is not squeezed so tightly as to alter its thickness. Care should be taken to see that the specimen is seated squarely between the anvil and the spindle; if it is at all skewed it can lead to very serious errors.

**4.**

The micrometer used here is graduated in inches and each numbered division on the fixed scale represents one-tenth (0·1) of an inch. These divisions are sub-divided into four so that each small division represents one-fortieth (0·025) of an inch. The moving scale is graduated from 0 to 25 and one fixed scale small division is uncovered by turning the thimble through one revolution. Hence 25 moving scale divisions represent 0·025 ($\frac{1}{40}$) inches or 1 moving scale division represents 0·001 ($\frac{1}{1000}$) inches.

quarters of the division which is only partly uncovered. Each of these represents 0·025 inch. Finally we read the number on the moving scale nearest to the line engraved on the sleeve. This gives the numbers of moving scale divisions, each of which represents 0·001 inches. Then the three readings are added. In this example a fixed scale reading of 1 large division, 3 small (quarter) divisions and a moving scale reading of 15 divisions adds up to 0·1 in. + 0·075 in. + 0·015 in. giving a total 0·190 inches. If the micrometer shows 3 large divisions, 2 small (quarter) divisions and 7 moving scale divisions, the thickness of that specimen is read as 0·3 + 0·05 + 0·007, giving a total of 0·357 inches.

**5.**

To read the micrometer we first note the number of large (0·1 inch) divisions that are completely uncovered on the sleeve. Next we count the

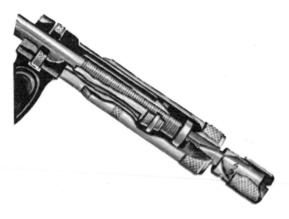

**6.**

A cutaway to show the screw thread on the concealed end of the spindle. This turns in the matching screw thread inside the sleeve.

# Index